Collins
revision guides

ActiveRevision

GCSEMaths
Intermediate

■ **Paul Metcalf**

■ Series editor: Jayne de Courcy

CONTENTS

CONTENTS

	In specification	Revise again	Revised & understood

ABOUT THIS BOOK AND CD-ROM

HOW THIS BOOK WILL HELP YOU

ActiveRevision GCSE Maths is an entirely new way to revise and boost your GCSE grade. The book and CD-ROM work interactively to help you assess your strengths, target your weaknesses and polish your skills.

ActiveRevision GCSE Maths Intermediate will help you to prepare for your exam by:

- presenting all the topics in an easy-to-revise format (**Book**)
- testing you on your knowledge and understanding (**CD-ROM**)
- highlighting mistakes you should avoid (**Book**)
- helping you to approach exam questions with confidence (**Book and CD-ROM**)
- helping you to plan your revision time effectively (**CD-ROM**).

WHAT THE BOOK CONTAINS

Key topics
This book covers all the topics that you need for GCSE Maths Intermediate level. Each topic is covered clearly and concisely. There are numerous worked examples to help your understanding. You should be able to work through each topic in no more that 15–20 minutes.

Common mistakes
These boxes highlight the mistakes that examiners see most frequently each year when marking students' exam papers. By reading through these boxes carefully, you can ensure that you **avoid making these errors** and losing valuable marks.

Pre-tests and final tests
Each batch of units has a linked pre-test and final test. These are on the CD ROM (see pages 6–9). They allow you to check how well you understand the topic **before** reading through the unit and then check your understanding **after** revising the unit.

Exam practice
This section gives you invaluable guidance on how to answer exam questions well. There is a **calculator paper** and a **non-calculator paper**. Answers and hints are given at the back of the book.

HOW TO MAKE THE BEST USE OF THIS BOOK AND CD-ROM

Everyone has their own strengths and weaknesses so the way that you use **ActiveRevision GCSE Maths** is up to you. You can decide which of these approaches suits you better:

Option 1 – Work steadily through the book and CD-ROM

1. Obtain a copy of your GCSE exam specification from your teacher. Then, on the **contents list** at the start of this book, tick off all the units you need to cover.

2. One by one, complete each unit in the book by doing the **pre-test**, reading the **unit** and then doing the **final test** on the CD-ROM.

3. If you don't score high marks on a final test, tick the **'revise again'** column in the contents list. This will help you keep track of the areas on which you need to spend more time.

4. If you do score high marks on a test, tick the **'revised and understood'** column of the contents list.

5. Once you have done most of the tests, the **Revision Planner** on the CD-ROM will help you to prioritise the areas on which you need to spend further revision time.

Option 2 – Concentrate on your weak areas first

If you are short of time, you could opt for a more selective approach to your Maths revision. In this case you could:

1. Obtain a copy of your GCSE exam specification from your teacher. Then, on the **contents list** at the start of this book, tick off all the units you need to cover.

2. Decide which areas you think are your weakest and try the relevant **pre-tests** on the CD-ROM.

3. If you don't score high marks on these tests, read through the units in the book and then do the **final tests** for these topics.

4. If you have time, try the pre-tests for some of the areas you feel confident about too, just to check you're not being over-confident!

5. Once you have done most of the tests, the **Revision Planner** on the CD-ROM will help you to prioritise the areas on which you need to spend further revision time.

Remember, whichever option you choose, use the book and CD-ROM interactively to get instant feedback on your strengths and weaknesses.

HOW TO INSTALL YOUR CD-ROM

To run the ActiveRevision application, you just need to double-click on the file called `ar.exe` (or `ar.hqx` if you're using a Mac) on the CD-ROM. On some computers it will start automatically when you put the disc into the CD-ROM drive.

If the application then appears in a small window, you can hold down the CTRL key and press F to make it fill the whole screen.

> For minimum requirement to run the CD-ROM, see page 128.

1. WELCOME SCREEN

This is the first screen that you will see. Once the data has finished loading, click on the **"Continue"** button to get to the Main Menu.

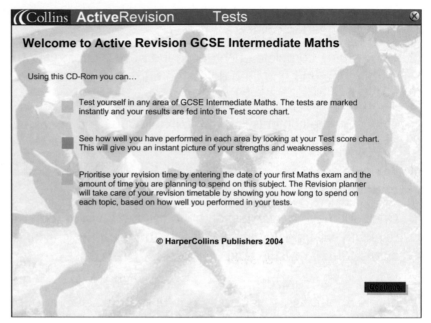

Welcome screen

2. MAIN MENU

You can select tests in four areas: **Number, Algebra, Shape, Space and Measures** and **Handling Data**. Just click on the one you want to do.

Alternatively, click on one of the buttons at the bottom of the screen and this will take you to your **Test Score Chart** or the **Revision Planner** (see page 9).

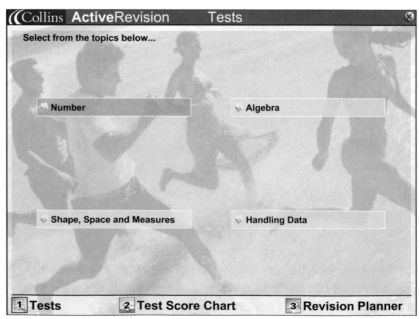

Main menu

3. THE TESTS

Selecting the test you want
Once you have selected your test topic, you will see all the the tests (preliminary and final) listed for that topic. Just click on the one you want!

Answering the questions
Each test consists of about 6–10 questions. Each question tells you exactly what you have to do and gives you invaluable practice in the skills you need for your exam. (For some questions, you may need plain paper for working, or graph paper for drawing a graph. And a pen or pencil.) If you want to redo a question before submitting your answer, click on the **"Restart Question"** button.

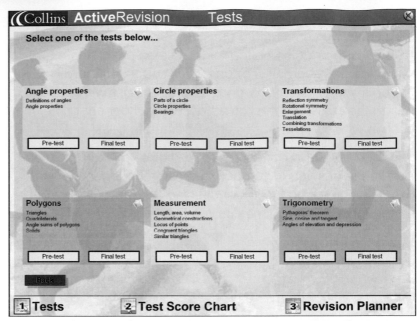

Test selection menu

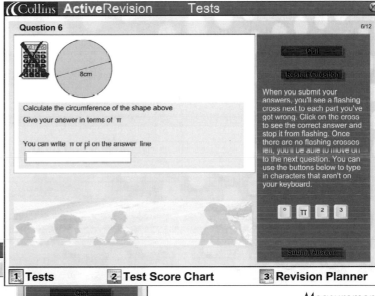

Measurement question screen

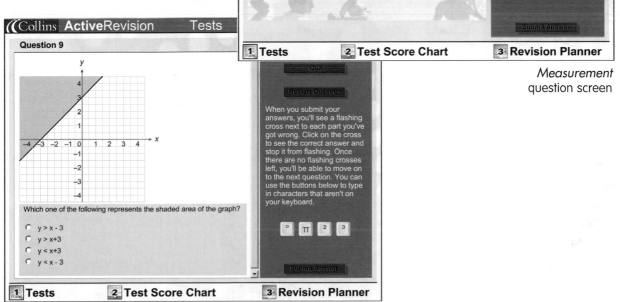

Drawing graphs question screen

Instant feedback

When you have completed a question, just click on the **"Submit Answer" button** at the bottom of the screen or use the return key on your keyboard. If your answer is correct, a tick will appear. If your answer is wrong, a flashing cross will appear. Click on the cross and the correct answer will appear in the question window. The cross(es) will change to tick(s).

A **Quick Tip** will also appear, which will give you extra help or reiterate the answer. To compare the correct answer with your own answer, click on the tick again. You can move backwards and forwards as many times as you like.

To go on to the next question, click on the **"Next >" button**. Or, if you want to return to the test selection menu, click on the **"Quit" button**. (Note: you must close the **Quick Tip** box so that it disappears before you can move on.)

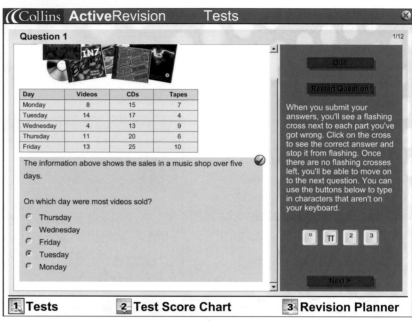

Representing data 1 question screen

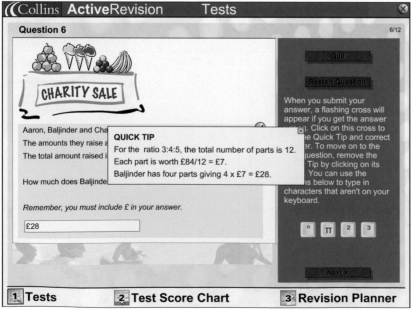

Number 2 question screen

4. TEST SCORE CHART

Once you have completed all the questions in a test, your marks are fed into the **Test Score Chart** so that you have **a record of which tests you have completed and how well you have done**. Your results are colour-coded so you can see at a glance which areas you understand well and which areas need further work. Remember, if you think it will help, **you can redo a test** – perhaps after going back over the relevant unit in the book. The **Test Score Chart** will keep a record of **your latest score only**.

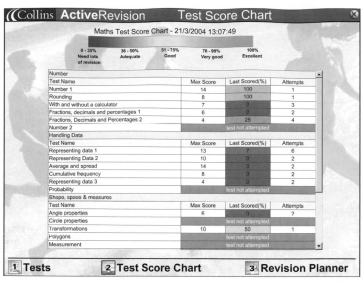

Test Score Chart

5. REVISION PLANNER

Once you have completed most of the tests, the **Revision Planner** will help you **prioritise your remaining Maths revision time**. All you have to do is enter the date of your first Maths exam, and how many hours you want to revise Maths per week. You will then be shown the areas on which it might be best for you to spend your remaining revision time – based on how you have performed in the tests. The **Revision Planner changes as you complete or redo tests**, and as you get nearer to the exam.

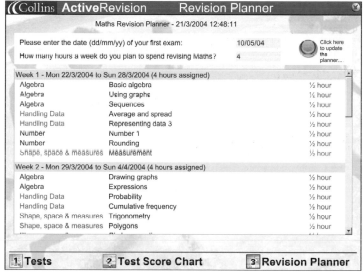

Revision Planner

THE NUMBER SYSTEM

DEFINITION OF NUMBERS

- You can describe sets of numbers in many different ways:
  natural numbers   1, 2, 3, 4, 5, ...
  positive integers $^+1, ^+2, ^+3, ^+4, ^+5, ...$
  negative integers $^-1, ^-2, ^-3, ^-4, ^-5, ...$
- Although **zero** is neither positive nor negative, it is still an integer.
- Other sets of numbers you need to know include:
  square numbers   1, 4, 9, 16, 25, 36, ...

  triangle numbers   1, 3, 6, 10, 15, 21, ...

... HINT ...

- Impress your teachers and your friends by remembering these definitions.

MULTIPLES

- The **multiples** of a number are the products in its multiplication table.

  Multiples of 3 are 3, 6, 9, 12, 15, 18, 21, 24, ...
  Multiples of 4 are 4, 8, 12, 16, 20, 24, 28, 32, ...

- The **least common multiple** (**LCM**) of two or more numbers is the lowest multiple that is common to, or shared by, all of the given numbers.

  Common multiples of 3 and 4 are 12, 24, 36, ...
  The least common multiple (LCM) is 12.

... HINTS ...

- The least common multiple is often called the lowest common multiple.
- In this sense, something that is common is shared.

FACTORS

- The **factors** of a number are all the natural numbers that divide exactly into that number, without leaving a remainder.

  Factors of 8 are 1, 2, 4 and 8.
  Factors of 12 are 1, 2, 3, 4, 6 and 12.

- The **highest common factor** (**HCF**) is the highest factor that is common to, or shared by, all of the given numbers.

  Common factors of 8 and 12 are 1, 2 and 4.
  The highest common factor is 4.

PRIME NUMBERS

- A **prime number** is a natural number that has exactly two factors, which are 1 and itself.

> These numbers have exactly two factors so they are prime numbers.   2, 3, 5, 7, 11, 13, 17, 19, 23, 29, 31, …

PRIME FACTORS

- A **prime factor** is a factor that is also a prime number.
- Any natural number can be written as a **product of its prime factors**.

> 21 can be written as 3×7 where 3 and 7 are prime factors.
> 60 can be written as $2 \times 2 \times 3 \times 5$ where 2, 3 and 5 are prime factors.

- You can find the prime factors of a number by repeatedly rewriting it as a product of prime numbers in increasing order (2, 3, 5, 7, 11, 13, 17, …).

> | | |
> |---|---|
> | $84 = 2 \times 42$ | Writing 84 as 2×42. |
> | $\quad = 2 \times 2 \times 21$ | Writing 42 as 2×21. |
> | $\quad = 2 \times 2 \times 3 \times 7$ | Writing 21 as 3×7. |

• • • HINT • • •

- You can always check your answer by multiplying out.

- You can show this in a **factor tree**. You start by writing each number as a product of two factors, then write these factors as products of two factors, and so on, until the numbers at the ends of the branches are all prime factors of the original number.
- There are usually several ways of making factor trees.

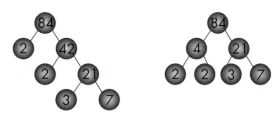

- When you have repeated factors, you can use **index notation**.

> | | |
> |---|---|
> | $168 = 2 \times 84$ | Writing 168 as 2×84. |
> | $\quad = 2 \times 2 \times 42$ | Writing 84 as 2×42. |
> | $\quad = 2 \times 2 \times 2 \times 21$ | Writing 42 as 2×21. |
> | $\quad = 2 \times 2 \times 2 \times 3 \times 7$ | Writing 21 as 3×7. |
> | $\quad = 2^3 \times 3 \times 7$ | Using index notation (see page 12). |

• • • HINTS • • •

In the examples above, you could also write:
- $60 = 2^2 \times 3 \times 5$
- $84 = 2^2 \times 3 \times 7$.

INDEX FORM AND INDICES

POWERS

- 'Index' is a singular word. The plural is 'indices'.

- When you multiply a number by itself you can use a **power** or **index** to write it in a short and neat way.
- You write the power or index as a small number at the top right of the **base** – the number you are multiplying.

5^3 means $5 \times 5 \times 5$	5 is the base, 3 is the power or index.
5^4 means $5 \times 5 \times 5 \times 5$	
5^{10} means $5 \times 5 \times 5 \times 5 \times 5 \times 5 \times 5 \times 5 \times 5 \times 5$	

COMMON ✗ MISTAKES

- **Don't multiply the base by the power.**
$2^5 = 2 \times 2 \times 2 \times 2 \times 2$
$5^2 = 5 \times 5$
- **These are wrong!**
$2^5 = 10$ ✗
$5^2 = 10$ ✗

- When you multiply a number by itself, you write it down like this.
$7 \times 7 = 7^2$
You say '7 to the power 2' (or '**7 squared**').
$7 \times 7 \times 7 = 7^3$
You say '7 to the power 3' (or '**7 cubed**').

MULTIPLYING INDICES

- You can multiply numbers that are written with indices.

$$7^4 \times 7^6 = (7 \times 7 \times 7 \times 7) \times (7 \times 7 \times 7 \times 7 \times 7 \times 7)$$
$$= 7 \times 7 \times 7 \times 7 \times 7 \times 7 \times 7 \times 7 \times 7 \times 7$$
$$= 7^{10}$$

- When you want to multiply two numbers that can be written with indices, and they both have the same base, you can use the quick method of just adding their powers.

- Multiplying and dividing numbers expressed with indices are popular topics for examination questions.

$7^4 \times 7^6 = 7^{4+6} = 7^{10}$ and in general:
$a^m \times a^n = a^{m+n}$

DIVIDING INDICES

- You can divide numbers with indices, if they both have the same base, like this.
$$5^6 \div 5^4 = \frac{5 \times 5 \times 5 \times 5 \times 5 \times 5}{5 \times 5 \times 5 \times 5} = 5 \times 5 = 5^2$$

- When you want to divide one number by another, and they can both be written as powers of the same base, you can use the quick method and just subtract their powers.
$5^6 \div 5^4 = 5^{6-4} = 5^2$ and in general:
$a^m \div a^n = a^{m-n}$

NEGATIVE INDICES

- You should know that $8^4 \div 8^6 = 8^{4-6} = 8^{-2}$

  and $8^4 \div 8^6 = \dfrac{8 \times 8 \times 8 \times 8}{8 \times 8 \times 8 \times 8 \times 8 \times 8} = \dfrac{1}{8^2}$

  so $8^2 = \dfrac{1}{8^{-2}}$.

- In general:

$$a^{-m} = \frac{1}{a^m}$$

$$3^{-2} = \frac{1}{3^2} = \frac{1}{9}$$

$$2^{-4} = \frac{1}{2^4} = \frac{1}{16}$$

ZERO INDICES

- You should know that $5^2 \div 5^2 = 5^{2-2}$
  $$= 5^0$$

  and $5^2 \div 5^2 = \dfrac{5 \times 5}{5 \times 5}$
  $$= 1$$

  so $5^0 = 1$.

- In general:

$$a^0 = 1$$

$5^0 = 1$, $100^0 = 1$, $2.5^0 = 1$ and $(-6)^0 = 1$

- **The rules of indices – a summary**

$$a^m \times a^n = a^{m+n}$$

$$a^m \div a^n = a^{m-n}$$

$$a^{-m} = \frac{1}{a^m}$$

$$a^0 = 1$$

• • • HINTS • • •

- **Any number raised to the power zero is equal to 1.**

- **If you really want to make a mathematician cry, ask them what 0^0 is. Luckily this question won't appear on your examination paper!**

SQUARES, CUBES, ROOTS AND RECIPROCALS

SQUARES

- You get a **square number** when you multiply a number by itself.

The square of 8 is $8 \times 8 = 64$ and 64 is a square number.

CUBES

- You get a **cube number** when you multiply a number by itself, then multiply the result by the same number again.

The cube of 5 is $5 \times 5 \times 5 = 125$ and 125 is a cube number.

SQUARE ROOTS

- The **square root** of a number (such as 36) is the number (in this case, 6) which, when squared, gives the original number.

The square root of 36 is 6 (because $6 \times 6 = 36$).

$$\sqrt[2]{36} \text{ or } \sqrt{36} = 6$$

CUBE ROOTS

- The **cube root** of a number (such as 27) is the number (in this case 3) which, when cubed, gives the original number.

The cube root of 27 is 3 (because $3 \times 3 \times 3 = 27$).

$$\sqrt[3]{27} = 3$$

RECIPROCALS

- You can find the **reciprocal** of any number (apart from zero) by converting the number to a fraction and turning the fraction upside-down.

The reciprocal of $\frac{2}{3}$ is $\frac{3}{2}$.

The reciprocal of 10 is $\frac{1}{10}$ $\left(\text{as } 10 = \frac{10}{1}\right)$.

NUMBER 1
FINAL TEST

ROUNDING

ROUNDING PRE-TEST

SIGNIFICANT FIGURES

- You can **round** any number to a given number of **significant figures** (written s.f.).
- Use these rules for rounding to a given number of significant figures.
  - Count along to the number of significant figures you require.
  - Look at the **next** digit to the right.
    If its value is smaller than 5, leave the significant digits as they are.
    If its value is 5 or greater, add 1 to the last of the significant digits.
  - Restore the number to its right size by padding with zeros if necessary.

Round 738.27 to 4, 3, 2, 1 significant figures.
738.27 = 738.3 (4 s.f.)
738.27 = 738 (3 s.f.)
738.27 = 740 (2 s.f.)*
738.27 = 700 (1 s.f.)*
You need to pad the numbers marked with an asterisk (*) with zeros in order to restore the numbers to their right size.

DECIMAL PLACES

- You can **round** any number to a given number of **decimal places** (written d.p.).
- Use these rules for rounding to a given number of decimal places.
  - Count along to the number of decimal places required.
  - Look at the digit in the **next** decimal place.
    If its value is smaller than 5, leave the preceding digits (the digits before it) as they are.
    If its value is 5 or greater, add 1 to the preceding digit.
  - Restore the number by rewriting any numbers to the **left** of the decimal point.

Round 206.2483 to 4, 3, 2, 1 decimal places.
206.2483 = 206.2483 (4 d.p.)
206.2483 = 206.248 (3 d.p.)
206.2483 = 206.25 (2 d.p.)
206.2483 = 206.2 (1 d.p.)
The numbers to the left of the decimal point are not affected by this rounding process as you are only concerned with decimal places and these all come after the decimal point.

ROUNDING FINAL TEST

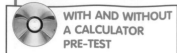

WITH AND WITHOUT
A CALCULATOR
PRE-TEST

MENTAL METHODS

ADDITION AND SUBTRACTION

There are several different ways to add and subtract **mentally**.

● You could split the numbers and use **place value**.

> Add 49 + 32
> Split the numbers like this.
> $$40 + 9 + 30 + 2$$
> $$= 40 + 30 + 9 + 2$$
> $$= 70 + 11$$
> $$= 81$$

● Consider using a **number line**.

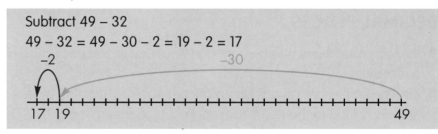

> Add 49 + 32
> $$49 + 30 + 2 = 79 + 2 = 81$$

● Similarly for subtraction.

> Subtract 49 − 32
> $$49 − 32 = 49 − 30 − 2 = 19 − 2 = 17$$

● ● ● HINTS ● ● ●

● One of your examination papers will require you to work without a calculator.

● Practise working without a calculator wherever you can.

● These examples illustrate some common non-calculator methods.

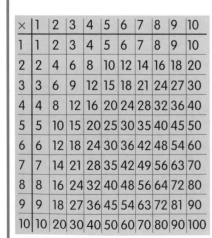

MULTIPLICATION

● You need to know your tables for this work.
● You should know that multiplication is the same as **repeated addition**.

> $$6 \times 5 = 5 + 5 + 5 + 5 + 5 + 5 = 30$$
> You might say, 'Six lots of 5' for 6×5.

● You can tackle harder multiplication like this.

$$63 \times 7 = (60 + 3) \times 7$$
$$= (60 \times 7) + (3 \times 7)$$
$$= 420 + 21$$
$$= 441$$

Remember that 60×7 is the same as $6 \times 10 \times 7$ or $6 \times 7 \times 10$

- Similarly

  $63 \times 24 = (60 + 3) \times 24$

  $ = 60 \times 24 + 3 \times 24$

  $ = 60 \times (20 + 4) + 72$

  $ = 60 \times 20 + 60 \times 4 + 72$

  $ = 1200 + 240 + 72$

  $ = 1512$

  Remember that 3×24 is the same as $3 \times 2 \times 12 = 72$.

  Remember that 60×20 is the same as:

  $6 \times 10 \times 2 \times 10 = 1200$

  or $6 \times 2 \times 10 \times 10 = 1200$.

- Or

  $63 \times 24 = 63 \times (20 + 4)$

  $ = 63 \times 20 + 63 \times 4$

  $ = 1260 + 252$

  $ = 1512$

- You can also use the **grid method** for multiplication.

  $63 \times 24 = 1200 + 60 + 240 + 12 = 1512$

×	60	3
20	1200	60
4	240	12

• • • HINT • • •

- It is more usual to set this multiplication out like this.

  ```
      63
  ×   24
    1260   Multiplying by 20
  +  252   Multiplying by 4
    1512   Adding
  ```

DIVISION

- You should know how to divide by a one-digit number.

Divide $301 \div 7$

```
    4 3
7)30²1
```

```
    43
7)301     7 into 30 gives 4 r 2.
  28↓
   21     Bring down the 1.
   21     7 into 21 gives 3.
    0
```

- To divide by a two-digit number, proceed in exactly the same way.

Divide $513 \div 19$

You could lay it out like this.

```
        2 7
19)51¹³3
```

It is more usual to set it out like this, though.

```
    27
19)513
   38↓
   133
   133
     0
```

COMMON ✗ MISTAKE

- Take care with the alignment of the numbers and always be sure to bring them down in the correct columns, otherwise you will get a silly answer.

USING A CALCULATOR

WHAT TYPE IS YOURS?

- 3 + 8 × 5 = 43 but
  (3 + 8) × 5 = 55
- You must work out the parts in the brackets first.
- If there are no brackets in the question, then multiplication comes before addition. This is why the same numbers seem to give different answers.

- For the examination you will need to know how to '**use calculators effectively and efficiently**'.
- There are many different types of calculator around, so check that you know how to use yours.
- You will need a **scientific calculator** for the examination.
- Try this out on your calculator.
  3 + 8 × 5
  Your answer should be 43.
  If your answer is 55 then you are not using a scientific calculator.

KNOW HOW IT WORKS

- Read the user manual.
  You will find nearly all of the **functions** on the opposite page on most calculators, but your manual will provide further information.
- Check – you may need to use an INV or 2ndF key to get into some of the functions you will need.

CHECKING AND ESTIMATION

- When you use a calculator you should always check your answers to make sure that they are reasonable.
- **Estimation** and **approximation** are common examination questions.
- You will usually be expected to give an estimation by **rounding numbers to one significant figure**.

- Always round your numbers correct to one significant figure (1 s.f.) then calculate an estimate.
- Do not calculate the answer and then round off.

Estimate the value of $\dfrac{6.98 \times (10.16)^2}{9.992 \times \sqrt{50}}$

Rounding the figures to 1 s.f. and approximating $\sqrt{50}$ as 7:

$$\frac{6.98 \times (10.16)^2}{9.992 \times \sqrt{50}} = \frac{7 \times 10^2}{10 \times 7}$$

$$= \frac{700}{70}$$

$$= 10$$

Your calculator should give an answer of 10.197 777 so this approximation is quite good.

Key	Explanation
C	Cancel – cancels only the last number entered.
AC	All cancel – cancels all of the data entered.
x^2	Calculates the square of the number.
x^3	Calculates the cube of the number.
$\sqrt{}$	Calculates the square root of the number.
$3\sqrt{}$	Calculates the cube root of the number.
π	This key gives the number π so you do not need to type in all of the decimal places.
$1/x$ or x^{-1}	Calculates the reciprocal of the number.
+/–	Reverses the sign by changing positive numbers to negative numbers and negative numbers to positive numbers.
x^y	This is the power key. To enter 3^6 you key in 3 x^y 6
(or)	The bracket keys allow you to change the order of a calculation. The calculator works out the contents of the brackets first.
EXP or EE	This is the standard form button. To enter 3.2×10^7 you key in 3 . 2 EXP 7 The display will show 3.2 ^{07} or 3.2 07
$a^b/_c$	This is the fraction key (not all calculators have this key). To enter $\frac{3}{4}$ key in 3 $a^b/_c$ 4 . 3⌋4 in the display means $\frac{3}{4}$. To enter $1\frac{3}{4}$ key in 1 $a^b/_c$ 3 $a^b/_c$ 4 . 1⌋3⌋4 in the display means $1\frac{3}{4}$.
Min or STO	Stores the displayed value in the memory.
MR or RCL	Recalls the value stored in the memory.
M+	Adds the displayed value to the number in the memory.
M–	Subtracts the displayed value from the number in the memory.
Mode	Gives the mode for calculations – refer to your user manual.
DRG	Gives the units for angles (degrees, radians or grads). Your calculator should normally be set to degrees.

IMPERIAL AND METRIC UNITS

UNITS OF MEASURE

- The system of measurements uses imperial and metric units.

Measure	Imperial units	Metric units
Length	inch (") foot (') yard (yd) mile	millimetre (mm) centimetre (cm) metre (m) kilometre (km)
Capacity	fluid ounce (fl oz) pint (pt) gallon (gall)	millilitre (ml) litre (l) kilolitre (kl)
Weight	ounce (oz) pound (lb) stone (st) hundredweight (cwt) ton	milligram (mg) gram (g) kilogram (kg) tonne (t)

- These tables show the relationships between the units.

Imperial measure		
Length	12 inches (in)	= 1 foot (ft)
	3 feet	= 1 yard (yd)
	1760 yards	= 1 mile
Capacity	20 fluid ounces (fl oz)	= 1 pint (pt)
	8 pints	= 1 gallon (gall)
Weight	16 ounces (oz)	= 1 pound (lb)
	14 pounds	= 1 stone (st)
	8 stones	= 1 hundredweight (cwt)
	20 hundredweights	= 1 ton

Metric measure		
Length	10 millimetres (mm)	= 1 centimetre (cm)
	100 centimetres	= 1 metre (m)
	1000 millimetres	= 1 metre
	1000 metres	= 1 kilometre (km)
	10 millilitres (ml)	= 1 centilitre (cl)
Capacity	1000 millilitres	= 1 litre
	1000 milligrams	= 1 gram
Weight	1000 grams	= 1 kilogram (kg)
	1000 kilograms	= 1 tonne (t)

CONVERSION FACTORS

- You will also need to know how to convert between imperial and metric units. This table will help.

Imperial	Metric
1 inch	2.5 cm
1 foot	30 cm
5 miles	8 kilometres
1.75 pints	1 litre
1 gallon	4.5 litres
2.2 pounds	1 kilogram

COMPOUND MEASURES

WHAT ARE COMPOUND MEASURES?

- Compound measures involve more than one unit, such as **speed** (distance and time) or **density** (mass and volume).

SPEED

- The formula for speed is

$$\text{speed} = \frac{\text{distance}}{\text{time}}$$

- The formula for speed can be rearranged:

distance = speed × time

or

$$\text{time} = \frac{\text{distance}}{\text{speed}}$$

> A taxi travels 16 miles in 20 minutes.
> What is the speed in miles per hour?
> As the speed is measured in miles per hour, express the distance in miles and the time in hours.
> Time = 20 minutes = $\frac{1}{3}$ hour
>
> $$\text{Speed} = \frac{\text{distance}}{\text{time}} = \frac{16}{1/3} = 48 \text{ mph}$$

> A cyclist travels 3.6 km at an average speed of 8 kilometres per hour. How long does the journey take?
>
> $$\text{Time} = \frac{\text{distance}}{\text{speed}} = \frac{3.6}{8} = 0.45 \text{ hours} = 27 \text{ minutes}$$

DENSITY

- The formula for density is

$$\text{density} = \frac{\text{mass}}{\text{volume}}$$

- The formula for density can be rearranged:

mass = density × volume

or

$$\text{volume} = \frac{\text{mass}}{\text{density}}$$

> A piece of lead weighing 170 g has a volume of 15 cm^3.
> Give an estimate for the density of lead.
>
> $$\text{Density} = \frac{\text{mass}}{\text{volume}} = \frac{170}{15} = 11.3 \text{ g/cm}^3 \text{ (3 s.f.)}$$

COMMON ✗ MISTAKES

- **0.45 hours is not 45 minutes as there are 60 minutes in one hour.**
- **To convert hours to minutes, multiply by 60.**
- **0.45 hours = 0.45 × 60 minutes = 27 minutes**
- **The journey takes 27 minutes.**

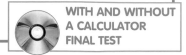

WITH AND WITHOUT
A CALCULATOR
FINAL TEST

FRACTIONS, DECIMALS AND PERCENTAGES 1 PRE-TEST

••• HINTS •••

- Always check that your answers are reasonable, especially in questions on this topic.
- Remember the difference between adding fractions and multiplying fractions.
- Make sure that you can do both.

FRACTIONS

WHAT IS A FRACTION?

- A fraction is a way of describing **part of a whole**.
- The top part of a fraction is called the **numerator** and the bottom part is called the **denominator**.

$$\frac{1}{2} \begin{array}{l} \leftarrow \text{numerator} \\ \leftarrow \text{denominator} \end{array}$$

EQUIVALENT FRACTIONS

- Equivalent fractions are fractions that are **equal in value**. These fractions are all equivalent to $\frac{1}{2}$.

$$\frac{1}{2} = \frac{2}{4} = \frac{3}{6} = \frac{5}{10} = \ldots$$

- You can find equivalent fractions by multiplying or dividing the numerator and denominator by the **same number**.

$$\overset{\times 10}{\frac{3}{4}} = \frac{30}{40} \qquad \overset{\times 3}{\frac{4}{7}} = \frac{12}{21} \qquad \overset{\div 2}{\frac{160}{200}} = \frac{80}{100} \qquad \overset{\div 3}{\frac{9}{12}} = \frac{3}{4}$$

ONE NUMBER AS A FRACTION OF ANOTHER

- To find one number as a fraction of another, write the numbers in the form of a fraction.

Write 4 mm as a fraction of 8 cm.
First ensure that the units are the same.
Remember 8 cm = 80 mm.
4 mm as a fraction of 80 mm = $\frac{4}{80} = \frac{1}{20}$
So 4 mm is $\frac{1}{20}$ of 8 cm.

ADDITION AND SUBTRACTION OF FRACTIONS

- You can only add or subtract fractions if they have the **same denominator**. Look for the **lowest common denominator**.

$$\frac{7}{8} - \frac{1}{5}$$
$$= \frac{35}{40} - \frac{8}{40} \qquad \text{Writing both fractions with a}$$
$$= \frac{27}{40} \qquad \text{denominator of 40, } \frac{7}{8} = \frac{35}{40} \text{ and } \frac{1}{5} = \frac{8}{40}.$$

- To find the lowest common denominator of two fractions, you need to find the **least common multiple** or LCM of their denominators. The LCM of 8 and 5 is 40 (see page 10).

COMMON ✗ MISTAKE

- You cannot add or subtract fractions simply by adding or subtracting the numerators and then adding or subtracting the denominators.

MULTIPLICATION OF FRACTIONS

- To multiply fractions, you can just multiply the **numerators** and multiply the **denominators**.

$\frac{4}{7} \times \frac{2}{11}$

$= \frac{4 \times 2}{7 \times 11}$ Multiplying the numerators and multiplying the denominators.

$= \frac{8}{77}$

$1\frac{1}{5} \times 6\frac{2}{3}$

$= \frac{6}{5} \times \frac{20}{3}$ Converting to top-heavy fractions.

$= \frac{6 \times 20}{5 \times 3}$ Multiplying the numerators and multiplying the denominators.

$= \frac{120}{15} = 8$

- Remember to **cancel** the fractions where possible.

- $1\frac{1}{5} \times 6\frac{2}{3}$

$= \frac{{}^{2}\cancel{6}}{{}_{1}\cancel{5}} \times \frac{\cancel{20}^{4}}{\cancel{3}_{1}}$

$= \frac{2}{1} \times \frac{4}{1}$

$= 2 \times 4 = 8$

DIVISION OF FRACTIONS

- To divide one fraction by another, you multiply the first fraction by the **reciprocal** of the second fraction.

$\frac{3}{7} \div \frac{1}{7}$

$= \frac{3}{{}_{1}\cancel{7}} \times \frac{\cancel{7}^{1}}{1}$ Cancelling the fractions.

$= 3$ As $\frac{3}{1} = 3$.

$4\frac{4}{5} \div 1\frac{1}{15}$

$= \frac{24}{5} \div \frac{16}{15}$ Converting to top-heavy fractions.

$= \frac{{}^{3}\cancel{24}}{{}_{1}\cancel{5}} \times \frac{\cancel{15}^{3}}{\cancel{16}_{2}}$ Changing the ÷ to × and turning the second fraction upside-down.

$= \frac{3 \times 3}{1 \times 2}$

$= \frac{9}{2}$

$= 4\frac{1}{2}$ Rewriting as a mixed number.

HINTS

- Remember the different ways in which fractions and parts of fractions may be described.
- A top-heavy fraction is one in which the numerator (top) is bigger than the denominator (bottom).
- You may see a top-heavy fraction called an improper fraction.
- A mixed number is made up of a whole number and a fraction.
- Any mixed number can be changed to an improper fraction.
- Any improper fraction can be changed to a mixed number.

DECIMALS

PLACE VALUE

- Decimal numbers consist of a **whole number part** and a **fractional part**.

decimal point

43.527

whole number part — fractional part

- The whole-number part is to the **left** of the decimal point. The fractional part is to the **right** of the decimal point.
- The **places** in the fractional part to the right of the decimal point represent $\frac{1}{10}, \frac{1}{100}, \frac{1}{1000}, \ldots$.

$\quad$ 10 $\quad$ 1 $\qquad \frac{1}{10} \frac{1}{100} \frac{1}{1000}$

43.527

The number 43.527 represents:

4 tens, 3 units, 5 tenths, 2 hundredths and 7 thousandths

- Say the number 43.527 as 'forty-three point five two seven', never as 'forty-three point five hundred and twenty-seven'.
- A decimal number like this is like a **mixed number** in fractions.

ADDITION AND SUBTRACTION OF DECIMALS

- When you add or subtract decimals, you must always make sure that the numbers are **lined up properly**, according to their **place value**.
- This is easy to do if you always make sure that the **decimal points** are lined up.

Add 8.61 + 43.527

$$
\begin{array}{r}
8.61 \\
+ \ 43.527 \\
\hline
52.137
\end{array}
$$

Subtract 16.75 − 3.22

$$
\begin{array}{r}
16.75 \\
- \ 3.22 \\
\hline
13.53
\end{array}
$$

COMMON ✗ MISTAKE

- **Be careful when you are working with decimals. It is easy to forget that 0.2 is bigger than 0.199.**

MULTIPLYING DECIMALS

To multiply two decimal numbers **without using a calculator**:
- **ignore the decimal points** and **multiply the numbers**
- add the **number of digits after the decimal points** in the numbers in the question
- position the decimal point so that the number of digits **after** the decimal point in the answer is the **same** as the **total number of decimal places in the question**.

Multiply 1.67×5.3

$167 \times 53 = 8851$ Ignoring the decimal points and multiplying the numbers.

The total number of digits after the decimal point in the numbers = $2 + 1 = 3$.

$1.67 \times 5.3 = 8.851$ Replacing the decimal point so that the number of digits after the decimal point in the answer is 3.

- You should always check that the answer is **approximately correct**. 1.67×5.3 is approximately $2 \times 5 = 10$ so the answer of 8.851 looks right.

DIVIDING DECIMALS

- You can use the idea of **equivalent fractions** to divide decimals.

Work out $0.003\,08 \div 0.000\,14$.

$$0.003\,08 \div 0.000\,14 = \frac{0.003\,08}{0.000\,14}$$

$$= \frac{308}{14}$$

Multiplying top and bottom by 100 000 to obtain an equivalent fraction.

Now divide $308 \div 14$.

```
        22
   14)308
      28↓
      ‾‾
       28
       28
       ‾‾
        0
```

So $0.003\,08 \div 0.000\,14 = 22$

PERCENTAGES

WHAT ARE PERCENTAGES?

••• HINTS •••

- 'Per cent' means 'per hundred'.
- This makes it easy to think of a percentage as a fraction 'out of a hundred'.

- Percentages are fractions with a **denominator of 100**.
  1% means 1 out of 100 or $\frac{1}{100}$

  25% means 25 out of 100 or $\frac{25}{100}$

  and $\frac{25}{100}$ is $\frac{1}{4}$ in its lowest terms.

PERCENTAGE CHANGE

- You can work out a percentage change by first working out the change and then using the formula:

  $$\text{percentage change} = \frac{\text{change}}{\text{original amount}} \times 100\%$$

  where the change might be an increase, decrease, profit, loss or error.

PERCENTAGE OF AN AMOUNT

- You can find the percentage of an amount if you find **1% of the amount** and then **multiply** to find the required amount.

COMMON MISTAKES

- Make sure you know how to find a percentage. Don't just divide by 100.
- Make sure you know how to find one number as a percentage of another. 30 as a percentage of 40 is

  $\frac{30}{40} \times 100 = 75\%$.

The value of an investment of £72 increases by 12%.
What is the new amount of the investment?

$$1\% \text{ of } £72 = £\frac{72}{100}$$

$$= £0.72$$
$$12\% \text{ of } £72 = 12 \times £0.72$$
$$= £8.64$$

The new amount is £72 + £8.64 = £80.64

- Alternatively, you can use the fact that after a 12% **increase**, the new amount is 100% of the original amount **plus** 12% of the original amount or 112% of the original amount.
  The new value of the investment is 112% of £72.

  $$1\% \text{ of } £72 = £0.72$$
  $$112\% \text{ of } £72 = 112 \times £0.72$$
  $$= £80.64 \text{ (as before)}$$

- Similarly, a **decrease** of 12% = 100% of the original amount **minus** 12% of the original amount which makes it 88% of the original amount.

FRACTIONS, DECIMALS AND PERCENTAGES 1 FINAL TEST

REVERSE PERCENTAGES

FRACTIONS, DECIMALS AND PERCENTAGES 2 PRE-TEST

- If you increase an amount by 10%, then decrease the new amount by 10%, you do **not** get back to the original amount.

  Increasing a price of £10 by 10%:

  $$£10 + 10\% \text{ of } £10 = £10 + \tfrac{10}{100} \times £10$$
  $$= £10 + £1$$
  $$= £11$$

  Decreasing a price of £11 by 10%:

  $$£11 - 10\% \text{ of } £11 = £11 - \tfrac{10}{100} \times £11$$
  $$= £11 - £1.10$$
  $$= £9.90$$

- You can use reverse percentages to find the **original amount** after a percentage change.

••• HINT •••

- In questions that involve reverse percentages you are given the amount after the percentage change has been applied.

A television is advertised for sale at £335.75 after a price reduction of 15%. What was the original price?

£335.75 represents 85% of the original price (100% – 15%)

So 85% of the original price = £335.75

1% of the original price = $£\dfrac{335.75}{85}$

$= £3.95$

100% of the original price = 100 × £3.95
$= £395$

The original price of the television was £395.

A telephone bill costs £101.05 including VAT at $17\tfrac{1}{2}$%.
What is the cost of the bill without the VAT?

£101.05 represents 117.5% of the bill (100% + 17.5%).

117.5% of the bill = £101.05

1% of the bill = $£\dfrac{101.05}{117.5}$

$= £0.86$

100% of the bill = 100 × £0.86
$= £86$

The telephone bill was £86 without the VAT.

COMMON ✗ MISTAKE

- Don't be put off by reverse percentages, but always check your answers by working backwards.

FRACTIONS, DECIMALS, PERCENTAGES

FRACTIONS TO DECIMALS

- You can change a fraction to a decimal by **dividing** the numerator by the denominator.

> Change $\frac{3}{8}$ to a decimal.
>
> $$\frac{3}{8} = 3 \div 8$$
> $$= 0.375$$

> Change $\frac{4}{15}$ to a decimal.
>
> $$\frac{4}{15} = 4 \div 15$$
> $$= 0.266\,666\,6\ldots$$

- The decimal 0.266 666 6... carries on **infinitely**. It is called a **recurring decimal**.
- You can write the recurring decimal 0.266 666 6... as $0.2\dot{6}$.
  The dot over the 6 means that the number 6 repeats infinitely.
- If a **group of numbers** repeats infinitely, you can use **two dots** to show the repeating numbers.
  $0.\dot{3}\dot{5} = 0.353\,535\,35\ldots$
  $6.4\dot{1}\dot{7} = 6.417\,171\,717\ldots$
  $3.\dot{2}0\dot{1} = 3.201\,201\,201\ldots$
  $11.60\dot{2}5\dot{3} = 11.602\,532\,532\,53\ldots$

••• HINTS •••

- You may find that you can recognise some of the recurring digit patterns.
- Look out for thirds, sixths, ninths, sevenths and so on.

COMMON ✗ MISTAKE

- Don't be put off by recurring decimals. They are only rational numbers, and rational numbers are just fractions.

DECIMALS TO FRACTIONS

- You can change a decimal to a fraction if you consider **place value**.

... 100	10	1	•	$\frac{1}{10}$	$\frac{1}{100}$	$\frac{1}{1000}$ ...
3	4	2	•	1	6	8

$$342.168 = 300 + 40 + 2 + \frac{1}{10} + \frac{6}{100} + \frac{8}{1000}$$

> Change 0.58 to a fraction.
>
> $0.58 = 0 \times 1$ and $5 \times \frac{1}{10}$ and $8 \times \frac{1}{100}$
> $$= 0 + \frac{5}{10} + \frac{8}{100}$$
> $$= \frac{50}{100} + \frac{8}{100} \quad \text{Rewriting as equivalent fractions with denominators of 100.}$$
> $$= \frac{58}{100}$$
> $$= \frac{29}{50} \quad \text{Cancelling.}$$

PERCENTAGES TO FRACTIONS

- You can change a percentage to a fraction by **dividing by 100**.

Change 65% to a fraction.

$65\% = \frac{65}{100} = \frac{13}{20}$ Cancelling.

Change $33\frac{1}{2}\%$ to a fraction.

$33\frac{1}{2}\% = \dfrac{33.5}{100} = \dfrac{67}{200}$ Changing the fraction to a decimal.
Multiplying top and bottom by 2.

FRACTIONS TO PERCENTAGES

- You can change a fraction to a percentage by **multiplying by 100**.

Change $\frac{1}{4}$ to a percentage.

$\frac{1}{4} = \frac{1}{4} \times 100\% = 25\%$

PERCENTAGES TO DECIMALS

- You can change a percentage to a decimal by **dividing by 100**.

Change 65% to a decimal.
$65\% = 65 \div 100 = 0.65$

DECIMALS TO PERCENTAGES

- You can change a decimal to a percentage by **multiplying by 100**.

Change 0.005 to a percentage.
$0.005 = 0.005 \times 100\% = 0.5\%$

COMPARING AND ORDERING

- You can **compare** and **order** percentages, fractions and decimals if you convert them all to percentages.

Put these numbers in order, starting with the smallest.
$26\%, \frac{1}{4}, 0.27$

Convert to percentages.
$26\% \rightarrow 26\%$
$\frac{1}{4} \rightarrow 25\%$
$0.27 \rightarrow 27\%$

In order, the numbers are $\frac{1}{4}$, 26%, 0.27.

... HINT ...

- You need to remove the half from the denominator and the easiest way to do this here is to multiply top and bottom by 2.

$$\frac{33.5}{100} \overset{\times 2}{\underset{\times 2}{=}} \frac{67}{200}$$

COMMON ✗ MISTAKES

- You must check whether the order is smallest to biggest or biggest to smallest. Don't lose marks by getting it wrong.
- Always give the numbers in the same form as they appear in the question. Don't leave them all as percentages.

SIMPLE INTEREST

WHAT IS INTEREST?

- Interest is an amount **paid** on money that is **deposited** in a bank or building society, or **invested** in any other way.

SIMPLE INTEREST

- For **simple interest**, the amount of interest paid is **not** reinvested.

- The formula for simple interest is:

$$I = \frac{PRT}{100}$$

and the **amount** is given by:

$$A = P + \frac{PRT}{100}$$

where I = **simple interest**

A = **total amount**

P = **principal** or **original investment**

R = **rate** (% per annum, or % p.a.)

T = **time** (in years).

••• HINTS •••

- Banks and building societies do not offer simple interest on their accounts.

- However, questions on simple interest often appear on the examination paper and they provide quite an easy way to gain marks.

£4000 is invested for 3 years at $4\frac{1}{2}$% p.a.
Calculate the simple interest and the total amount.

Using the formula $I = \dfrac{PRT}{100}$

where P = principal = £4000

R = rate = $4\frac{1}{2}$% or 4.5%

T = time = 3 years

$$I = \frac{4000 \times 4.5 \times 3}{100}$$

$= £540$

$A = P + I$ Amount = principal + interest.

$A = £4000 + £540$

$= £4540$

The simple interest is £540 and the total amount is £4540.

COMPOUND INTEREST

- With **compound interest**, the amount of interest paid is **reinvested** and **earns interest** itself.
- The formula for compound interest is:

$$A = P\left(1 + \frac{R}{100}\right)^T$$

where I = **simple interest**
A = **total amount**
P = **principal** or **original investment**
R = **rate** (% per annum, or % p.a.)
T = **time** (in years).

... HINTS ...

- You can find the compound interest by repeatedly applying the formula for simple interest.
- Alternatively, you can use the formula for compound interest if you can remember it.

£2500 is invested at 6.5% p.a. compound interest. What is the amount after 2 years?

You can calculate compound interest by repeatedly applying the simple interest formula.

$$A = P + \frac{PRT}{100}$$

where P = principal = £2500
R = rate = 6.5%
T = time = 1 year for each year.

Year 1 $A = 2500 + \dfrac{2500 \times 6.5 \times 1}{100}$

$= 2500 + 162.5$
$= £2662.50$ Writing £2662.5 as £2662.50

Year 2 $A = 2662.5 + \dfrac{2662.5 \times 6.5 \times 1}{100}$

As P = £2662.50 now.

$= 2662.5 + 173.0625$
$= 2835.5625$
$= £2835.56$ correct to the nearest penny.

Alternatively, you can use the compound interest formula.

$$A = P\left(1 + \frac{R}{100}\right)^T$$

$A = 2500\left(1 + \dfrac{6.5}{100}\right)^2$ As T = 2 years.

$= 2835.5625$
$= £2835.56$ correct to the nearest penny.

FRACTIONS, DECIMALS AND PERCENTAGES 2 FINAL TEST

NUMBER 2
PRE-TEST

DIRECTED NUMBERS

WHAT ARE DIRECTED NUMBERS?

- A **directed number** is one that has a + or − sign attached to it.
- You will see directed numbers used in temperature scales, where **negative numbers** show temperatures below freezing.

ADDING AND SUBTRACTING DIRECTED NUMBERS

- When you are adding or subtracting directed numbers, remember that signs written next to each other can be replaced by a **single sign**.

  + +   is the same as +   + −   is the same as −
  − +   is the same as −   − −   is the same as +

ADDING AND SUBTRACTING ON THE NUMBER LINE

$$^-1 + {^-}2 = {^-}1 - 2 = {^-}3 \qquad + - \text{ is the same as } -$$
$$^+2 - {^-}3 = {^+}2 + 3 = {^+}5 \qquad - - \text{ is the same as } +$$

- To add or subtract directed numbers, first find the **starting position**, then move **up** or **down** the number line.
  On a horizontal number line, move **right** or **left**.

$2 + 3 = {^+}5$	Start at $^+2$ and move up 3 places to $^+5$.	$^+2 \ ^+3 \ ^+4 \ ^+5$
$4 - 7 = {^-}3$	Start at $^+4$ and move down 7 places to $^-3$.	$^-3 \ ^-2 \ ^-1 \ 0 \ ^+1 \ ^+2 \ ^+3 \ ^+4$
$^-3 + 6 = {^+}3$	Start at $^-3$ and move up 6 places to $^+3$.	$^-3 \ ^-2 \ ^-1 \ 0 \ ^+1 \ ^+2 \ ^+3$
$^-1 - 4 = {^-}5$	Start at $^-1$ and move down 4 places to $^-5$.	$^-5 \ ^-4 \ ^-3 \ ^-2 \ ^-1$

MULTIPLYING AND DIVIDING DIRECTED NUMBERS

- To multiply or divide directed numbers, multiply or divide the numbers and then attach the sign according to these rules.
- If the signs are the same, the answer will be **positive**.
- If the signs are opposite, the answer will be **negative**.

$$^-8 \times {^+}2 = {^-}16 \qquad - \times + = -$$
$$^+12 \div {^-}4 = {^-}3 \qquad + \div - = -$$
$$^-2 \div {^-}5 = {^+}0.4 \qquad - \div - = +$$
$$^-(5)^2 = {^+}25 \qquad ^-(5)^2 = (^-5) \times (^-5) \text{ and } - \times - = +$$

••• HINTS •••

- When two signs appear together (e.g. 5 − $^-$4), replace them with one sign, using these rules.
- + + gives +
- + − gives −
- − + gives −
- − − gives +
- $^-1 + {^-}2$ is the same as $^-1 - 2$ since + − gives −.
- $^+2 - {^-}3$ is the same as $^+2 + 3$ since − − gives +.
- If a number has no sign with it, assume it is positive.

••• HINTS •••

- + × + gives +
- − × − gives +
- + × − gives −
- − × + gives −
- + ÷ + gives +
- − ÷ − gives +
- + ÷ − gives −
- − ÷ + gives −

RATIO AND PROPORTION

RATIO

- You can use a **ratio** to compare one quantity to another quantity, in a similar way to fractions.

> On a farm there are 12 dogs and 16 cats.
> The ratio of dogs to cats is 12 to 16, written as 12 : 16.

EQUIVALENT RATIOS

- Equivalent ratios are ratios that are **equal** to each other.
- These ratios are all equivalent to 2 : 5.
    2 : 5 = 4 : 10 = 6 : 15 = 8 : 20 = …
- You can find equivalent ratios by **multiplying** or **dividing** both sides of the ratio by the **same number**.

> Express the ratio 40p to £2 in its simplest form.
> You must ensure that the units are the same.
> Remember £2 = 200p.
> The ratio is 40 : 200 = 1 : 5 in its simplest form.
>   Dividing both sides of the ratio by 40.

PROPORTIONAL PARTS

- You can use ratios to divide amounts into **proportional** parts.
- To share an amount into proportional parts, **add** up all of the **individual** parts and **divide** the amount by this number to find the **value of one part**.

> £50 is to be divided between two sisters in the ratio 3 : 2.
> How much does each get?
>   Number of parts = 3 + 2
>   = 5
>   Value of each part = £50 ÷ 5
>   = £10
> The two sisters receive £30 (3 parts at £10 each)
> and £20 (2 parts at £10 each).

... HINTS ...

- The order of the numbers in a ratio is important.
- The ratio of cats to dogs is 16 to 12 or 16 : 12.

COMMON ✗ MISTAKES

- You should check that the amounts add up correctly. (£30 + £20 = £50)
- Don't throw marks away by forgetting to do a simple check like this.

STANDARD FORM NUMBERS

••• HINTS •••

- You can use standard form as a short way of writing very large numbers and very small numbers.

- Large numbers are written with positive powers of 10.

- Small numbers are written with negative powers of 10.

COMMON ✗ MISTAKE

- Remember that 3×10^5 is in standard form but 300×10^3 is not, since A must be between 1 and 10.

  You need to rewrite 300×10^3 as:

  $300 \times 10^3 = 3 \times 10^2 \times 10^3$
  (As $100 = 10^2$.)
  $= 3 \times 10^5$
  (As $10^2 \times 10^3 = 10^5$.)

STANDARD FORM

- A number in standard form is always written as:
  $$A \times 10^n$$
  where A lies between 1 and 10 and n is a **natural number**.

VERY LARGE NUMBERS

- You can write very large numbers as the product of a number between 1 and 10, and a **positive** power of 10.

> Write 267 000 000 in standard form.
> Write down 267 000 000 then place the decimal point so A lies between 1 and 10.
>
>
> 2.6 7 0 0 0 0 0 0
>
> To find n, count the 'power of 10'.
> Here, n = 8 so $267\,000\,000 = 2.67 \times 10^8$

VERY SMALL NUMBERS

- You can write very small numbers as the product of a number between 1 and 10, and a **negative** power of 10.

> Write 0.000 000 321 in standard form.
> Write down 0.000 000 321 then place the decimal point so A lies between 1 and 10.
>
> 0 0 0 0 0 0 3.21
>
> To find n in 0.000 000 321, count the 'power of 10'.
> Here, n = ⁻7 so $0.000\,000\,321 = 3.21 \times 10^{-7}$

ADDING AND SUBTRACTING IN STANDARD FORM WHEN POWERS ARE THE SAME

- It is very easy to add (or subtract) numbers in standard form **when the powers are the same**.

$(4.8 \times 10^{11}) + (3.1 \times 10^{11})$
$= (4.8 + 3.1) \times 10^{11}$
$= 7.9 \times 10^{11}$

$(4.63 \times 10^{-2}) - (2.7 \times 10^{-2})$
$= (4.63 - 2.7) \times 10^{-2}$
$= 1.93 \times 10^{-2}$

- To add (or subtract) numbers in standard form **when the powers are not the same**, you need to convert the numbers to ordinary form.

$(8.42 \times 10^{6}) + (6 \times 10^{7})$
$= 8\,420\,000 + 60\,000\,000$ Converting.
$= 68\,420\,000$
$= 6.842 \times 10^{7}$

MULTIPLYING AND DIVIDING

- To multiply (or divide) numbers in standard form, you need to use the **rules of indices**.

$(7.5 \times 10^{4}) \times (3.9 \times 10^{7})$
$= (7.5 \times 3.9) \times (10^{4} \times 10^{7})$ Collecting powers of 10.
$= 29.25 \times 10^{4+7}$ Using rules of indices.
$= 29.25 \times 10^{11}$
$= 2.925 \times 10^{12}$ As $29.25 = 2.925 \times 10^{1}$.

$(3 \times 10^{5}) \div (3.75 \times 10^{8})$
$= (3 \div 3.75) \times (10^{5} \div 10^{8})$ Collecting powers of 10.
$= 0.8 \times 10^{5-8}$ Using rules of indices.
$= 0.8 \times 10^{-3}$
$= 8 \times 10^{-4}$ As $0.8 = 8 \times 10^{-1}$.

... HINTS ...

Make sure you know the rules of indices.
- $10^{m} \times 10^{n} = 10^{m+n}$
- $10^{m} \div 10^{n} = 10^{m-n}$

NUMBER 2 FINAL TEST

BASIC ALGEBRA PRE-TEST

••• **HINT** •••

- Questions in algebra are quite straightforward if you follow the rules.

COMMON ✗ MISTAKE

- Don't panic if the letters used in the examination are not x and y. Any letters can stand for numbers.

LETTERS TO REPRESENT NUMBERS

- Algebra is just like arithmetic, except that you use **letters** to stand for numbers.

Suppose the area of this square is a.

This shape is twice the size of the square, so its area is
$a + a$ or $2 \times a$ or $2a$.

This shape is half the size of the square, so its area is
$\frac{1}{2} \times a$ or $\frac{1}{2}a$.

Suppose the area of the square is a and the area of the semicircle is b.

You can combine the two basic shapes to give different shapes.

The area of this shape is $a + b$.   The area of this shape is $a - b$.

The area of this shape is $2a + b$.

DEFINITIONS

- Any letter that you use to represent a number is called a **variable**.
  In the examples above, a and b are variables.
- Any number in front of a variable is called a **coefficient**.
  The number 2 in $2a + b$ is a coefficient.
- **Terms** are made up of coefficients and variables.
  $2a + b$ has two terms ($2a$ and b) and they are separated by a + sign.
- **Expressions** are collections of terms separated by + and – signs.
  $2a + b$ is an expression, and so are a, b, $2a$, $a + b$.

SIMPLIFYING AND SUBSTITUTING

- An **algebraic expression** is a collection of algebraic quantities, with their + and − signs.
- **Like terms** have the same variable but different coefficients.

  So $3x$, ^-5x, x and $\frac{1}{2}x$ are all like terms – they have the same variable (in this case x) but different coefficients.

  Similarly, $2xy$, $5x2y$, $^-20x2y$ and $x2y$ are all like terms – they have the same variable (in this case xy) but different coefficients.

SIMPLIFYING BY ADDING AND SUBTRACTING TERMS

- The process of adding and subtracting like terms in an expression (or an equation) is called **simplifying**.

$3x + 3y + 5x − 7y$
$= 3x + 5x + 3y − 7y$ Collecting together like terms.
$= 8x − 4y$

$5p − (4q − 2p)$
$= 5p − 4q + 2p$ As $− × − = +$ for the term in
$= 7p − 4q$ the brackets.

$4ab + 6a − 2b + 5ba$
$= 4ab + 5ab + 6a − 2b$ As $5ba$ is the same as $5ab$.
$= 9ab + 6a − 2b$

SIMPLIFYING BY MULTIPLYING AND DIVIDING TERMS

- Multiplying and dividing terms is also called simplifying.

Simplify these expressions.
$3p × 4q = 3 × 4 × p × q = 12pq$
$5a × 7a = 5 × 7 × a × a = 35a^2$ As $a × a = a^2$.

$8ab^2 ÷ 2ab = \dfrac{8ab^2}{2ab} = \dfrac{\overset{4}{\cancel{8}}\cancel{ab}b^2}{\underset{1}{\cancel{2ab}}} = 4b$ Cancelling top and bottom.

SUBSTITUTION

- Substitution means **replacing the letters** in an expression (or formula) by **given numbers**.

When $a = 3$, $b = 2$ and $c = 5$ then:
$a + b + c = 3 + 2 + 5 = 10$
$a × b × c = 3 × 2 × 5 = 30$
$b^2 + 2\dfrac{a}{c} = 2^2 + 2 × \dfrac{3}{5} = 4 + \dfrac{6}{5} = 5\dfrac{1}{5}$

ALGEBRAIC INDICES

• • • HINTS • • •

- Remember that the power or index tells you how many of the base number or letter there are.

- Make sure you learn these rules and don't muddle them up.

- You already know the **rules of indices**.

$$a^m \times a^n = a^{m+n}$$
$$a^m \div a^n = a^{m-n}$$

$$a^{-n} = \frac{1}{a^n}$$

$$a^0 = 1$$

So that:

$$3^6 \times 3^5 = 3^{6+5} = 3^{11}$$
$$12^9 \div 12^7 = 12^{9-7} = 12^2$$

$$4^{-2} = \frac{1}{4^2} = \frac{1}{16}$$

$$76^0 = 1$$

- The **same** laws of indices apply to algebra.

$$p^2 \times p^5 = p^{2+5}$$
$$= p^7$$
$$q^7 \div q^7 = q^{7-7}$$
$$= q^0 = 1 \qquad \text{As } q^0 = 1.$$
$$r^4 \times r \times r^{11} = r^{4+1+11}$$
$$= r^{16} \qquad \text{As } r = r^1.$$
$$s^3 \div s^5 = s^{3-5} = s^{-2}$$
$$= \frac{1}{s^2} \qquad \text{As } s^{-2} = \frac{1}{s^2}.$$

COMMON ✗ MISTAKE

- Make sure that you know which number or letter is the base and which is the power or index.

Simplify the expression $3p^3q^2 \times 4p^2q^4$.

$$3p^3q^2 \times 4p^2q^4 = 3 \times p^3 \times q^2 \times 4 \times p^2 \times q^4$$
$$= 3 \times 4 \times p^3 \times p^2 \times q^2 \times q^4$$
$$= 12 \times p^5 \times q^6$$
$$= 12p^5q^6 \quad \text{Using the rules of indices:}$$
$$p^3 \times p^2 = p^{3+2} = p^5$$
$$q^2 \times q^4 = q^{2+4} = q^6$$

BASIC ALGEBRA
FINAL TEST

EXPANDING AND FACTORISING 1

EXPRESSIONS
PRE-TEST

- You can use **brackets** to group **algebraic terms**.
- The process of removing the brackets is called **expanding**.
- The process of rewriting an expression including the brackets is called **factorising**.

EXPANDING BRACKETS

- When expanding brackets you must multiply all of the terms **inside** the brackets by the term **outside**.

Expand these expressions.
$3(p - 7q)$ $^-6(a - 2b)$

$$3(p - 7q) = 3 \times p + 3 \times {}^-7q$$
$$= 3p - 21q$$
$$^-6(a - 2b) = {}^-6 \times a - {}^-6 \times 2b$$
$$= {}^-6a + 12b$$

Expand and simplify this expression.
$$2a - 3(4b - 3a) = 2a - 3 \times 4b - 3 \times {}^-3a$$
$$= 2a - 12b + 9a$$
$$- 11a - 12b$$

FACTORISING INTO BRACKETS

- To factorise an expression, look for terms that have **common factors**.

Factorise these expressions.

$10a - 15$ $9rs + 12st$ $8ab^2 - 16a^2b$
$10a - 15 = 5(2a - 3)$
$9rs + 12st = 3s(3r + 4t)$
$8ab^2 - 16a^2b = 8ab(b - 2a)$

Simplify the expression $8a + 3(a + b) - 2(3a - b)$.

$$8a + 3(a + b) - 2(3a - b) = 8a + 3a + 3b - 6a + 2b$$
$$= 8a + 3a - 6a + 3b + 2b$$
$$= 5a + 5b$$
$$= 5(a + b)$$

Remember that $^-2 \times {}^-b = 2b$.

• • • HINT • • •

- You should always check your answers by expanding the brackets.

• • • HINT • • •

- To simplify completely, you must check that you cannot factorise your final answer any further.

39

EXPANDING AND FACTORISING 2

BINOMIAL EXPRESSIONS

••• HINT •••

- This area diagram shows how it works.

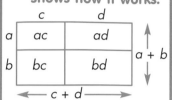

The area of $(a + b)(c + d)$ is the same as the total area of $ac + ad + bc + bd$.

So $(a + b)(c + d) = ac + ad + bc + bd$

- A **binomial expression** consists of two **terms**.
- $(a + b)$ and $(5x - 2z)$ are binomial expressions.
- To **expand** the product of two binomial expressions, multiply each term in the **first** expression by each term in the **second** expression.

$$(a + b)(c + d) = a(c + d) + b(c + d)$$
$$= a \times c + a \times d + b \times c + b \times d$$
$$= ac + ad + bc + bd$$

- Use **FOIL** as a reminder of how to expand binomial expressions.

F = First	$(a + b)(c + d)$	$a \times c$
O = Outsides	$(a + b)(c + d)$	$a \times d$
I = Insides	$(a + b)(c + d)$	$b \times c$
L = Last	$(a + b)(c + d)$	$b \times d$

EXPANDING QUADRATICS

••• HINT •••

- The sign $\neq$ means 'is not equal to'.

- A **quadratic expression** has the form $ax^2 + bx + c$ where $a \neq 0$.
- The product of two binominals may give a quadratic expression.

Expand $(x + 5)(x - 3)$

F = First	$(x + 5)(x - 3)$	$x \times x = x^2$
O = Outsides	$(x + 5)(x - 3)$	$x \times {}^-3 = {}^-3x$
I = Insides	$(x + 5)(x - 3)$	$5 \times x = 5x$
L = Last	$(x + 5)(x - 3)$	$5 \times {}^-3 = {}^-15$

	x	5
x	x^2	$5x$
$^-3$	^-3x	$^-15$

$$(x + 5)(x - 3) = x^2 - 3x + 5x - 15$$
$$= x^2 + 2x - 15$$

FACTORISING QUADRATICS

••• HINT •••

- These are the only pairs of numbers that multiply together to give $^+5$. With practice, you should find the numbers quite quickly.

- You can simply **reverse** the above process to factorise a quadratic into the **product of two brackets**.

Factorise $x^2 - 6x + 5$.
Write $x^2 - 6x + 5 = (x \quad)(x \quad)$ As $x \times x = x^2$.
Then search for two numbers that multiply together to give $^+5$.
Try substituting:
$^+1 \times {}^+5$ gives $^+5$ $(x + 1)(x + 5) = x^2 + 6x + 5$ ✗
$^-1 \times {}^-5$ gives $^+5$ $(x - 1)(x - 5) = x^2 - 6x + 5$ ✓

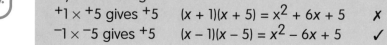

EXPRESSIONS FINAL TEST

SEQUENCES

- A **sequence** is a set of numbers that follow a **given rule**.
- The word **term** is often used to describe the numbers in the sequence.
- The expression **the nth term** describes a **general term** in the sequence.
- The **formula** for the nth term gives the value of **any term** in the sequence.
- The formula for the nth term of the sequence
  3, 7, 11, 15, 19, 23, …
  is $4n - 1$ so:

the first term ($n = 1$) is	$4 \times 1 - 1 = 3$
the second term ($n = 2$) is	$4 \times 2 - 1 = 7$
the third term ($n = 3$) is	$4 \times 3 - 1 = 11$
the 50th term ($n = 50$) is	$4 \times 50 - 1 = 199$
the 1000th term ($n = 1000$) is	$4 \times 1000 - 1 = 3999$ and so on.

- Most number sequences involve adding or subtracting, or multiplying or dividing, according to some rule.

LINEAR SEQUENCES

- In a linear sequence, the **differences between consecutive terms** are always the same.
- You can use this fact to find the nth term of a linear sequence.
  nth term = first term + $(n - 1) \times$ 1st difference

Find the formula for the nth term for this sequence.
3, 7, 11, 15, 19, 23, …
Work out the differences as shown.

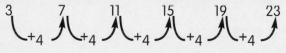

1st difference

The first differences are all the same so the sequence is linear.
Use the formula:

nth term $= 3 + (n - 1) \times 4$	Where 4 is the first difference.
$= 3 + 4n - 4$	Expanding the brackets.
$= 4n - 1$	Simplifying.

You should now check your answer to make sure it is correct.

1st term $= 4 \times 1 - 1 = 3$ ✓
2nd term $= 4 \times 2 - 1 = 7$ ✓
3rd term $= 4 \times 3 - 1 = 11$ ✓
6th term $= 4 \times 6 - 1 = 23$ ✓

SEQUENCES PRE-TEST

COMMON ✗ MISTAKE

- The rule for the nth term must work for all of the given values, not just the first few.

• • • HINT • • •

- For the linear sequence
  3, 7, 11, 15, 19, 23, …
  the first term is 3 and the second term is 7, the nth term is $4n - 1$.

• • • HINT • • •

- Don't just check the first few terms. Try one that comes later in the sequence, too.

SPECIAL SEQUENCES

NUMBER SEQUENCES

- You should be able to recognise some special sequences of numbers.

- Number, page 10, gives more information about these special sequences.

- 1, 4, 9, 16, 25, …   **square numbers**

- The rule for the nth term of the square numbers n^2.
- 1, 8, 27, 64, 125, …   **cube numbers**
- 1, 3, 6, 10, 15, …   **triangle numbers**

COMMON ✖ MISTAKE

- You shouldn't need to write down all the values for diagrammatic sequences. Solve them by looking at the shapes.

- The rule for the nth term of the triangle numbers is $\frac{1}{2}n(n + 1)$.
- 2, 3, 5, 7, 11, 13, 17, …   **prime numbers**
- There is no rule for the nth term of the series of prime numbers.

QUADRATIC SEQUENCES

- In a quadratic sequence the **first differences** are not the same.
- The formula for the nth term of a quadratic sequence includes a term in n^2.
- You should be able to recognise some quadratic sequences.

	nth term
1, 4, 9, 16, 25, …	n^2
2, 5, 10, 17, 26, …	$n^2 + 1$
0, 3, 8, 15, 24, …	$n^2 - 1$
2, 8, 18, 32, 50, …	$2n^2$

but watch out for:

0, 1, 4, 9, 16, …	$(n - 1)^2$

and

4, 9, 16, 25, 36, …	$(n + 1)^2$

COMMON ✖ MISTAKE

- If a sequence looks familiar but some numbers are missing, experiment with the nth term – 4, 9, 16, 25, … is $(n + 1)^2$, not n^2.

- You should always check your answers to make sure they work for the given term.

**SEQUENCES
FINAL TEST**

SOLVING EQUATIONS

EQUATIONS 1
PRE-TEST

- The equals sign in an **algebraic equation** means that the expressions on either side have the same value.
- To maintain this balance, always make sure that whatever you do to **one side** of the equation you also do to the **other side**.

• • • HINTS • • •

- The equals sign is like a balance between the two sides.
- Whatever you do to one side you must also do to the other to keep the equation balanced.

Solve $x + 10 = 5$.
$x + 10 - 10 = 5 - 10$ Taking 10 from both sides.
$x = {}^-5$

Solve $x - 4.5 = 2$.
$x - 4.5 + 4.5 = 2 + 4.5$ Adding 4.5 to both sides.
$x = 6.5$

Solve $4x = 14$.
$\dfrac{4x}{4} = \dfrac{14}{4}$ Dividing both sides by 4.
$x = 3.5$

Solve $\dfrac{x}{3} = 7$.

$\dfrac{x}{3} \times 3 = 7 \times 3$ Multiplying both sides by 3.

$x = 21$

Solve $6(3x - 5) = 42$.
$6 \times 3x + 6 \times {}^-5 = 42$ Expanding the brackets.
$18x - 30 = 42$
$18x - 30 + 30 = 42 + 30$ Adding 30 to both sides.
$18x = 72$
$\dfrac{18x}{18} = \dfrac{72}{18}$ Dividing both sides by 18.
$x = 4$

Alternatively:
$6(3x - 5) = 42$
$6(3x - 5) \div 6 = 42 \div 6$ Dividing both sides by 6.
$3x - 5 = 7$
$3x - 5 + 5 = 7 + 5$ Adding 5 to both sides.
$3x = 12$
$\dfrac{3x}{3} = \dfrac{12}{3}$ Dividing both sides by 3
$x = 4$

SOLVING INEQUALITIES

- You can solve inequalities in exactly the same way as you solve equalities (or equations) except that when **multiplying or dividing by a negative number** you **must reverse the inequality sign**.

$4y + 6 < 26$

$4y + 6 - 6 < 26 - 6$ Taking 6 from both sides.

$\qquad 4y < 20$

$\qquad \dfrac{4y}{4} < \dfrac{20}{4}$ Dividing both sides by 4.

$\qquad y < 5$

On the number line it looks like this.

$y < 5$ ←————————○

‹—+——+——+——+——+——+——+——›
　　0　1　2　3　4　5　6

$5 - \dfrac{y}{2} \leqslant 9$

$5 - 5 - \dfrac{y}{2} \leqslant 9 - 5$ Subtracting 5 from both sides.

$\qquad -\dfrac{y}{2} \leqslant 4$

$\dfrac{y}{2} \times {}^-2 \geqslant 4 \times {}^-2$ Multiplying both sides by ⁻2 and reversing the sign.

On the number line it looks like this.

$y \geqslant {}^-8$ ●————————→

‹—+——+——+——+——+——+——+——›
⁻11 ⁻10 ⁻9 ⁻8 ⁻7 ⁻6 ⁻5

$7x < 8x + 5$

$7x - 8x < 8x - 8x + 5$ Subtracting 8x from both sides.

$\qquad {}^-x < 5$

$-x \times {}^-1 > 5 \times {}^-1$ Multiplying both sides by ⁻1 and

$\qquad x > {}^-5$ reversing the sign.

On the number line it looks like this.

$x > {}^-5$ ○————————→

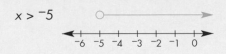

‹—+——+——+——+——+——+——+——›
⁻6 ⁻5 ⁻4 ⁻3 ⁻2 ⁻1 　0

REARRANGING FORMULAE

- You can rearrange (or **transpose**) a formula in exactly the same way as you solve an equation.
- To maintain the balance, you must make sure that whatever you do to **one side** of the formula you also do to the **other side**.
- In $y = mx + c$, y is the **subject** of the formula.
- You can rearrange the formula to make x the subject.

$y = mx + c$

$y - c = mx + c - c$ Subtracting c from both sides.

$y - c = mx$

$\dfrac{y - c}{m} = \dfrac{mx}{m}$ Dividing both sides by m.

$\dfrac{y - c}{m} = x$

$x = \dfrac{y - c}{m}$ Turning the formula around to make x the subject.

••• HINT •••

- Notice that you usually put the subject (x in the example) on the left-hand side.

In $S = \dfrac{D}{T}$, S is the subject of the formula.

Rearrange the formula to make

a D

b T the subject.

$ST = D$ Multiplying both sides of the formula by T.

$D = ST$ Turning the formula around to make D the subject.

Now, using $D = ST$:

$\dfrac{D}{S} = T$ Dividing both sides of the formula by S.

$T = \dfrac{D}{S}$ Turning the formula around to make T the subject.

Rearrange the formula $a = \sqrt{3b - 2}$ to make b the subject.

$a = \sqrt{3b - 2}$

$a^2 = 3b - 2$ Squaring both sides.

$a^2 + 2 = 3b$ Adding 2 to both sides.

$\dfrac{a^2 + 2}{3} = b$ Dividing both sides by 3.

$b = \dfrac{a^2 + 2}{3}$ Turning the formula around to make b the subject.

EQUATIONS 1
FINAL TEST

COORDINATES IN FOUR QUADRANTS

- The two **axes** on a graph divide the graph into **four quadrants**.
- The point where the axes cross is called the **origin**.
- You can use **coordinates** to locate any point on a graph.
- Coordinates are written in the form (x, y), where x is the distance from the origin along the **x-axis** (the horizontal axis) and y is the distance from the origin along the **y-axis** (the vertical axis).

Show the point with coordinates (4, 3) on a grid.

The point is:

4 units along the x-axis (the horizontal axis) and

3 units along the y-axis (the vertical axis).

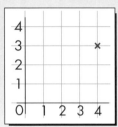

Show the point with coordinates (⁻3, ⁻5) on a grid.

The point is:

⁻3 units along the x-axis (3 units in the negative direction) and

⁻5 units along the y-axis (5 units in the negative direction).

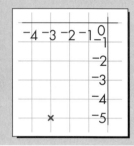

- This graph shows A(4, 3), B(⁻3, ⁻5), C(2, ⁻6) and D(⁻3, 1).

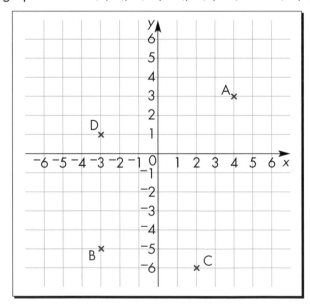

USING COORDINATES

- You can use coordinates to:
  - draw a graph, by **plotting points** lying on the graph
  - draw a shape, by **plotting coordinates of the vertices** (corners)
  - show the **centre of a transformation**.

LINEAR GRAPHS

- Linear means **straight line** so all linear graphs are straight lines.

GRADIENT OF A STRAIGHT LINE

- The **gradient** of a straight line is a measure of its slope.
- The gradient of a line that slopes **up** from bottom left to top right is **positive**. For a line that slopes **down** from top left to bottom right the gradient is **negative**.

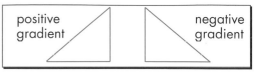

- **Parallel** lines have the same gradient, and lines with the same gradient are parallel.
- You can work out the gradient of any straight line by looking at two points and working out the **vertical distance** between them and the **horizontal distance** between them.
- Then the gradient of the line is defined as:

$$\frac{\text{vertical distance}}{\text{horizontal distance}}$$

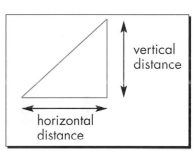

- The equation for any straight line can be written in the form $y = mx + c$ where m is the gradient of the straight line and c is the **cut-off** on the y-axis (also called the y-**intercept**).
- In the diagram, the equation is $y = 2x - 1$, so $m = 2$ and $c = {}^{-}1$.

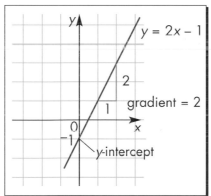

Calculate the gradient of the line segment joining $({}^{-}1, {}^{-}2)$ and $(3, 10)$.

The gradient of a line is defined as:

$$\frac{\text{vertical distance between two points}}{\text{horizontal distance between the points}}$$

$$= \frac{10 - {}^{-}2}{3 - {}^{-}1} = \frac{12}{4} = 3$$

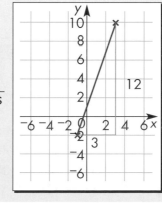

... HINT ...

- A line segment is just a part of a line.

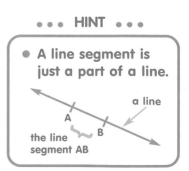

INTERPRETING GRAPHS

- For the examination, you may be asked to interpret a graph such as a **conversion** graph or a **travel** graph.

CONVERSION GRAPHS

- A conversion graph showns a **direct relationship between two variables,** such as dollars and pounds.
- You can draw a conversion graph to show a direct relationship.
- You can use a conversion graph to **convert** from one variable to the other.

Draw a conversion graph to show the relationship between miles and kilometres, given that 5 miles is approximately 8 kilometres.
Use your graph to convert:

a 15 miles to kilometres

b 8 miles to kilometres

c $32\frac{1}{2}$ kilometres to miles.

• • • HINTS • • •

5 miles ≈ 8 kilometres
10 miles ≈ 16 kilometres
20 miles ≈ 32 kilometres

- **As this is a straight-line graph, three points will be sufficient (two for the line and one as a check) to draw the graph. As 0 miles is equal to 0 kilometres, the straight line goes through the origin.**

- **The sign ≈ means 'is approximately equal to'.**

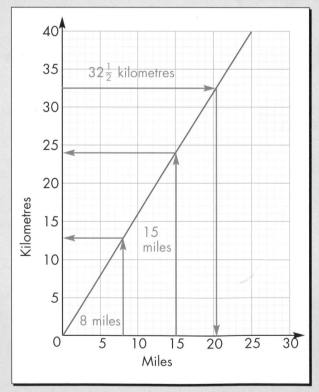

From the graph:

a 15 miles ≈ 24 kilometres

b 8 miles ≈ 12.8 kilometres   (Each small square is 1 km.)

c $32\frac{1}{2}$ kilometres ≈ 20.3 miles   (Each small square is 1 mile.)

TRAVEL GRAPHS

- A travel graph shows a journey.
- The **time** is always shown along the **horizontal axis** and the **distance** is shown on the **vertical axis**.
- A horizontal part of the graph shows a time when the person or vehicle was **not moving**.

Ranjit leaves home at 1030 hours and his distance from home is shown on the graph.

a How many kilometres does he travel before the first stop?

b How long does it take him to reach the first stop?

c How far is he away from home at 1600 hours?

d What time does Ranjit arrive back at home?

e How far does he travel between 1200 hours and 1600 hours?

f What is his average speed between 1030 hours and 1130 hours?

g What is his average speed between 1300 hours and 1330 hours?

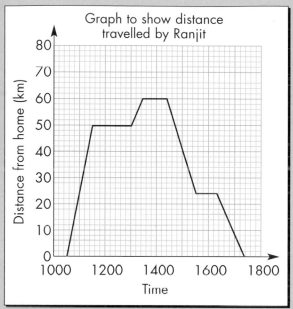

Graph to show distance travelled by Ranjit

a Ranjit travels 50 kilometres before the first stop.

b It takes 1 hour (from 1030 hours to 1130 hours.

c He is 24 kilometres away from home at 1600 hours.

d He arrives back home at 1718 hours. (Remember that each small square represents $\frac{1}{5}$ hour or 12 minutes.)

e He travels 10 km + 36 km = 46 km

f Between 1030 hours and 1130 hours:
   distance travelled = 50 km, time taken = 1 hour
   so speed = 50 kilometres per hour (speed = distance ÷ time)

g Between 1300 hours and 1330 hours:
   distance travelled = 10 km, time taken = $\frac{1}{2}$ hour
   so speed = 20 kilometres per hour (speed = distance ÷ time)

GRAPHING INEQUALITIES

- You can show **inequalities** on graphs quite easily by replacing the inequality sign with an equals (=) sign and drawing this line on the graph.
- You can define the **two regions** produced (one on either side of the line) by using **inequality signs**.
- You should usually **shade out the region which is not required**, although some examination questions ask you to shade the required region.
- You must make it clear to the examiner which is your required region, by **labelling** it appropriately.

... HINTS ...

- **You must make it clear whether the line is included.**
- **Use a solid line if the line is included (the inequality is ≤ or ≥).**
- **Use a dotted line if the line is excluded (the inequality is < or >).**

Draw graphs of these lines.
$$x = 2 \quad y = 1 \quad x + y = 6$$
Use the graphs to identify and label the region where the points (x, y) satisfy the inequalities:
$$x \geqslant 2 \quad y < 1 \quad x + y \leqslant 6$$

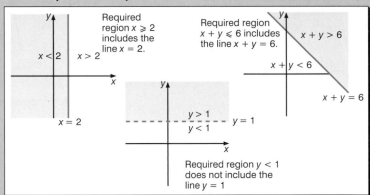

The required region is shown on the graph below and includes the adjoining parts of $x = 2$ and $x + y = 6$ but not the line $y = 1$ (which is dotted to make this clear to the reader or examiner).

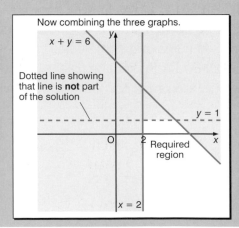

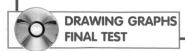

USING GRAPHS TO SOLVE SIMULTANEOUS EQUATIONS

- You can solve an equation such as $x + 2 = 6$ to give $x = 4$, as the equation has only one **variable**.
- You cannot solve an equation such as $y = x + 2$ as the equation has **two variables** and you need more information.
- A pair of equations with two unknown variables is a set of **simultaneous equations**.
- You can solve a pair of simultaneous equations by using algebra (see page 56) or by using graphs to plot the two equations.
- The **coordinates** of the **point of intersection** of the two lines give the **solutions** of the simultaneous equations.

> Solve these simultaneous equations. $\qquad y = x + 2$
> $\qquad\qquad\qquad\qquad\qquad\qquad\qquad\qquad y = 2x - 1$
>
> The line $y = x + 2$ has a gradient of 1 and cuts the y-axis at $^{+}2$.
> The line $y = 2x - 1$ has a gradient of 2 and cuts the y-axis at $^{-}1$.
> Draw the two lines on the same set of axes.
>
>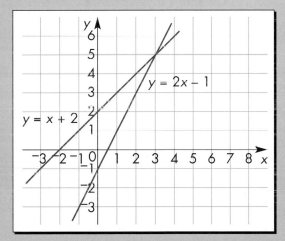
>
> The coordinates of the point of intersection, (3, 5), give the solutions of the simultaneous equations as $x = 3$ and $y = 5$.

••• HINT •••

- The algebraic method gives an exact solution, but the graphical method shows you the answer quickly.

- Always check the solutions by **substituting** them into the original pair of equations.

  When $x = 3$, $y = x + 2$ $\qquad$ in the first equation
  $\qquad\qquad\qquad = 3 + 2$
  $\qquad\qquad\qquad = 5 \qquad$ which is correct.
  When $x = 3$, $y = 2x - 1$ $\qquad$ in the second equation
  $\qquad\qquad\qquad = 2 \times 3 - 1$
  $\qquad\qquad\qquad = 5 \qquad$ which is correct.

COMMON ✘ MISTAKE

- Don't panic if the letters used in the examination are different. You can use any letters.

QUADRATIC GRAPHS

... HINTS ...

- If $a > 0$, the curve is this way up.

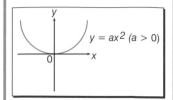

- If $a < 0$, the curve is this way up.

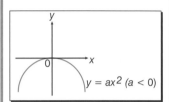

- When you draw these graphs, join up the points with a smooth curve, not a series of straight lines.

- Quadratic graphs are drawn from **quadratic equations** (see page 57). They are all the same basic shape.
- You can write the **equations** of quadratic graphs in the form:
  $y = ax^2 + bx + c$ (where a is non-zero).
- The diagram shows the graphs of:

$y = x^2$
$(a = 1, b = 0, c = 0)$
$y = x^2 + x - 6$
$(a = 1, b = 1,$
$c = ^-6)$
$y = ^-x^2 + 5x - 4$
$(a = ^-1, b = 5,$
$c = ^-4)$.

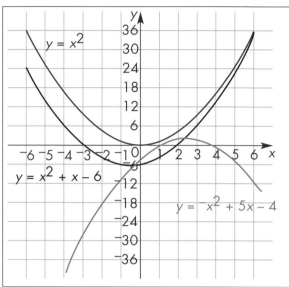

Draw the graph of $y = x^2 + x - 6$ and use it to solve the equation $x^2 + x - 6 = 0$.
Drawing up a table of values:

x	$^-5$	$^-4$	$^-3$	$^-2$	$^-1$	0	1	2	3
$y = x^2 + x - 6$	14	6	0	$^-4$	$^-6$	$^-6$	$^-4$	0	6
Coordinates	$(^-5, 14)$	$(^-4, 6)$	$(^-3, 0)$	$(^-2, ^-4)$	$(^-1, ^-6)$	$(0, ^-6)$	$(1, ^-4)$	$(2, 0)$	$(3, 6)$

To solve the equation $x^2 + x - 6 = 0$ you need to consider the points that lie on the curve
$y = x^2 + x - 6$ and on the line $y = 0$.
Any points that satisfy both of these equations will also satisfy the equation $x^2 + x - 6 = 0$.
From the graph you can see that $x^2 + x - 6 = 0$ when the curve crosses the line $y = 0$ (the x-axis), giving $x = ^-3$ and $x = 2$.
So $x = ^-3$ and $x = 2$ satisfy the equation $x^2 + x - 6 = 0$.

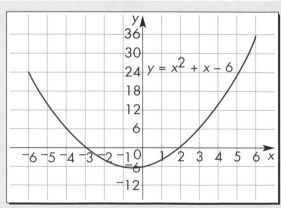

CUBIC GRAPHS

- Cubic graphs are drawn from **cubic equations** that have the form:
  $y = ax^3 + bx^2 + cx + d$ (where a is non-zero).
- This is the graph of **$y = x^3$**
  ($a = 1$).

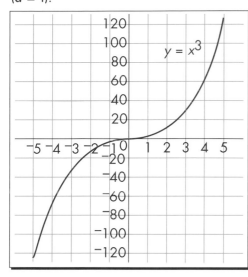

This is the graph of
$y = x^3 - 7x^2 + 14x - 8$
($a = 1$, $b = {}^-7$, $c = 14$,
$d = {}^-8$).

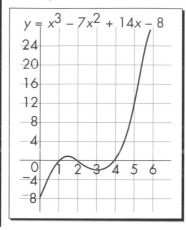

- If $a > 0$, the curve
  looks like this.

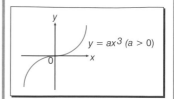

- If $a < 0$, the curve
  looks like this.

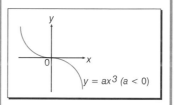

Draw the graph of $y = (x - 1)(x - 2)(x - 4)$ for $0 < x < 5$ and use it
to solve the equation $(x - 1)(x - 2)(x - 4) = 0$.
Drawing up a table of values:

x	0	0.5	1	1.5	2	2.5	3	3.5	4	4.5	5
y	${}^-8$	${}^-2.625$	0	0.625	0	${}^-1.125$	${}^-2$	${}^-1.875$	0	4.375	12
Coordinates	$(0, {}^-8)$	$(0.5, {}^-2.625)$	$(1, 0)$	$(1.5, 0.625)$	$(2, 0)$	$(2.5, {}^-1.125)$	$(3, {}^-2)$	$(3.5, {}^-1.875)$	$(4, 0)$	$(4.5, 4.375)$	$(5, 12)$

From the graph you can see that
$(x - 1)(x - 2)(x - 4) = 0$
when the curve crosses the line $y = 0$ (the x-axis),
giving $x = 1$, $x = 2$ and $x = 4$.
So that $x = 1$, $x = 2$ and $x = 4$ satisfy the equation
$(x - 1)(x - 2)(x - 4) = 0$.

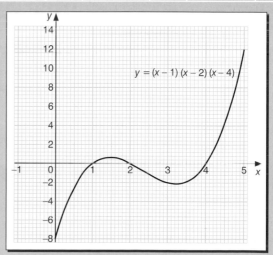

- If $a > 0$, the curve looks like this.

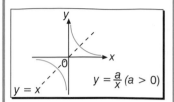
$$y = \frac{a}{x} \,(a > 0)$$
$$y = x$$

- If $a < 0$, the curve looks like this.

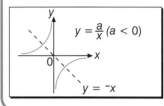
$$y = \frac{a}{x} \,(a < 0)$$
$$y = {}^-x$$

RECIPROCAL GRAPHS

- Reciprocal graphs are drawn from equations of the form $y = \frac{a}{x} + b$.

- The diagram shows the graphs of $y = \frac{2}{x}$ ($a = 2$, $b = 0$),

  $y = \frac{2}{x} + 5$ ($a = 2$, $b = 5$) and $y = 5 - \frac{2}{x}$ ($a = {}^-2$, $b = 5$)

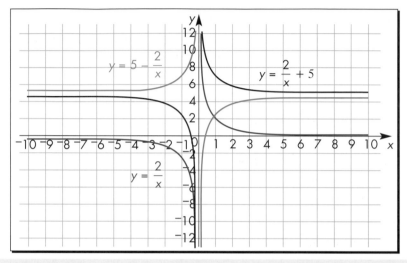

The graph of $xy = 12$ is the same as $y = \frac{12}{x}$ (or $x = \frac{12}{y}$).

It is not defined at $x = 0$ or $y = 0$.

On the same set of axes, draw the graph of $xy = 12$ and $y = x$. Use your graphs to solve the equation $x^2 = 12$.

Drawing up a table of values:

x	−4	−3	−2	−1	0	1	2	3	4
$y = x$	−4	−3	−2	−1	0	1	2	3	4
$y = \dfrac{12}{x}$	−3	−4	−6	−12		12	6	4	3

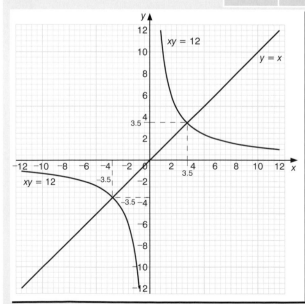

Use non-integer values, between 0 and 1, and 0 and ⁻1, to find out about the behaviour of the curve as it approaches the axes, and to draw its graph.

From the graph, the curve crosses the line $y = x$ when $x \approx {}^-3.5$ and $x \approx 3.5$ correct to 1 d.p.

So $x = {}^-3.5$ and $x = 3.5$ satisfy the equation $\frac{12}{x} = x$.

i.e. $12 = x \times x$ Multiplying both sides by x.

or $x^2 = 12$ As required.

USING GRAPHS
FINAL TEST

TRIAL AND IMPROVEMENT

EQUATIONS 2
PRE-TEST

- You can use trial and improvement to find successively better and better **approximations** to the solution of a problem.
- To find an initial approximation, it may help to **draw a graph** or try a few calculations (using whole numbers) in your head.

The length of a rectangle is 2 cm greater than its width and the area of the rectangle is 30 cm^2. Use trial and improvement to obtain a value for the width, correct to the nearest millimetre.

Width (cm)	Length (cm)	Area (cm^2)	Comments
4	6	24	too small
5	7	35	too large

Width must lie between 4 and 5.

4.5	6.5	29.25	too small

Width must lie between 4.5 and 5 (near to 4.5).

4.7	6.7	31.49	too large

Width must lie between 4.5 and 4.7.

4.6	6.6	30.36	too large

Width must lie between 4.5 and 4.6.

4.55	6.55	29.8025	too small

Width must lie between 4.55 and 4.6.

Since 4.55 and 4.6 are both equal to 4.6 (correct to the nearest millimetre), you can stop and say that the width of the rectangle is 4.6 cm (correct to the nearest millimetre).

Given that a solution of the equation $x^3 - 3x = 25$ lies between 3 and 4, use trial and improvement to obtain an answer correct to 1 decimal place.

When $x = 3$ $x^3 - 3x = 3^3 - 3 \times 3 = 18$
When $x = 4$ $x^3 - 3x = 4^3 - 3 \times 4 = 52$
Solution lies between 3 and 4 (closer to $x = 3$).
Try $x = 3.5$ $x^3 - 3x = 3.5^3 - 3 \times 3.5 = 32.375$
Solution lies between 3 and 3.5 (closer to $x = 3.5$).
Try $x = 3.3$ $x^3 - 3x = 3.3^3 - 3 \times 3.3 = 26.037$
Solution lies between 3 and 3.3 (closer to $x = 3.3$).
Try $x = 3.2$ $x^3 - 3x = 3.2^3 - 3 \times 3.2 = 23.168$
Solution lies between 3.2 and 3.3.
Try $x = 3.25$ $x^3 - 3x = 3.25^3 - 3 \times 3.25 = 24.578\,125$
Solution lies between 3.25 and 3.3.
Since 3.25 and 3.3 are both equal to 3.3 (correct to 1 decimal place), you can stop and say that the solution is 3.3 (correct to 1 decimal place).

USING ALGEBRA TO SOLVE SIMULTANEOUS EQUATIONS

METHOD OF SUBSTITUTION

- Rewrite one equation to make one of the unknowns the **subject**. **Substitute** for this unknown into the second equation and solve it.

Solve these equations.

$$x - 4y = 11$$
$$3x + 4y = 1$$

Rewrite $x - 4y = 11$ as $x = 11 + 4y$.

Now substitute this value of x into the second equation.

$$3x + 4y = 1$$
$$3(11 + 4y) + 4y = 1$$
$$33 + 12y + 4y = 1$$
$$33 + 16y = 1$$
$$16y = {}^-32$$
$$y = {}^-2$$

Now substitute this value of y into $x = 11 + 4y$.

$$x = 11 + 4 \times {}^-2$$
$$x = 3$$

The solution is $x = 3$ and $y = {}^-2$.

METHOD OF ELIMINATION

- You need to add or subtract the equations, or multiples of them, to **eliminate** one of the unknowns, then solve the resulting equation.

Solve these equations.

$$x - 4y = 11$$
$$3x + 4y = 1$$

Add the left-hand sides of both equations together to eliminate y.

$$(x - 4y) + (3x + 4y) = 11 + 1$$
$$x + 3x = 12$$
$$4x = 12$$
$$x = 3$$

Substitute this value in the first equation.

$$x - 4y = 11$$
$$3 - 4y = 11$$
$${}^-4y = 8$$
$$y = {}^-2$$

The solution is $x = 3$ and $y = {}^-2$.

QUADRATIC EQUATIONS

- Quadratic equations are equations of the form $ax^2 + bx + c = 0$ where $a \neq 0$.
- You can **solve** quadratic equations in a number of ways but at this level they are usually solved by **graphical** (see page 51) or **algebraic** methods.
- To solve quadratic equations algebraically, you need to know that **if the product of two numbers is zero** then **one or both of the numbers must be zero**.
  If $ab = 0$ then **either** $a = 0$ or $b = 0$, **or** both $a = 0$ and $b = 0$.
- First, you must write the quadratic equation in the form $ax^2 + bx + c = 0$, then split the **quadratic expression** into two **factors** (see page 40).
- Each factor will give a **solution** of the equation.

... HINT ...

- The sign $\neq$ means 'is not equal to'.

Solve the quadratic equation $(x - 5)(x + 3) = 0$.
Use the fact that since the product of the two brackets is zero then the expression inside one or both of them must be zero.

i.e. either $(x - 5) = 0$ which implies that $x = 5$
  or $(x + 3) = 0$ which implies that $x = {}^-3$.

So the solutions of the equation $(x - 5)(x + 3) = 0$ are $x = 5$ and $x = {}^-3$.

COMMON ✗ MISTAKE

- A quadratic equation has two solutions and you must give both. If the quadratic is a perfect square, it has two equal solutions.

Solve the quadratic equation $x^2 - 6x - 27 = 0$.
To solve the equation, factorise the left-hand side of the equation and then solve as before.
Factorising the left-hand side of the equation:
$x^2 - 6x - 27 = (x \quad)(x \quad)$
Now search for two numbers that multiply together to give $^-27$.

Try substituting:

$^+1 \times {}^-27$ gives $^-27$:	$(x + 1)(x - 27)$	$= x^2 - 26x - 27$ ✗
$^-1 \times {}^+27$ gives $^-27$:	$(x - 1)(x + 27)$	$= x^2 + 26x - 27$ ✗
$^+9 \times {}^-3$ gives $^-27$:	$(x + 9)(x - 3)$	$= x^2 + 6x - 27$ ✗
$^-9 \times {}^+3$ gives $^-27$:	$(x - 9)(x + 3)$	$= x^2 - 6x - 27$ ✓

The quadratic equation can be written as $(x - 9)(x + 3) = 0$.
Since the product of the two brackets is zero then the expression inside one or both of them must be zero.
i.e. either $(x - 9) = 0$ which implies that $x = 9$
  or $(x + 3) = 0$ which implies that $x = {}^-3$.
The solutions of $x^2 - 6x - 27 = 0$ are $x = 9$ and $x = {}^-3$.

... HINT ...

- Always check your answers by substituting them into the original equation.

EQUATIONS 2 FINAL TEST

ANGLE PROPERTIES
PRE-TEST

SOME DEFINITIONS

- You need to **know and understand** these definitions, as you will need them in your study of shape and space.

POINTS AND LINES

- A **point** is where two lines meet.

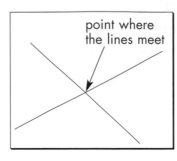

point where the lines meet

- Two lines (or planes) are **perpendicular** if they meet at a right angle.

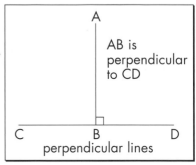

A

AB is perpendicular to CD

C   B   D

perpendicular lines

- A **line** is where two planes meet. JK is the line where the two planes meet.

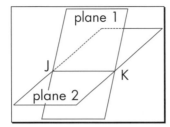

plane 1

J

K

plane 2

- Two lines or planes are **parallel** if they are the same perpendicular distance apart everywhere.

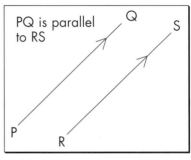

PQ is parallel to RS

Q

S

P

R

TYPES OF ANGLE

- **Angles** are formed whenever two or more lines meet.
- An angle is a **measure of turn**.
- Angles have special names depending on their size.
- You measure angles with a **protractor** or **angle measurer**.

- A **right angle** is equal to 90°.

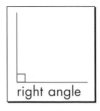

right angle

- An **obtuse angle** is more than 90° but less than 180°.

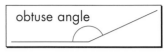

obtuse angle

- An **acute angle** is less than 90°.

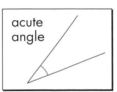

acute angle

- A **reflex angle** is more than 180° but less than 360°.

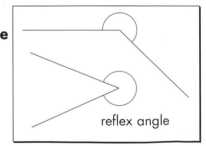

reflex angle

ANGLE PROPERTIES

- Different types of angle have different properties.
- **Complementary angles** add up to 90°.

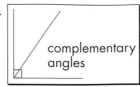

complementary angles

- **Supplementary angles** add up to 180°.

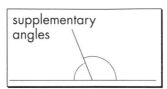

supplementary angles

ANGLES ON A STRAIGHT LINE AND AT A POINT

- Angles **on a straight line** add up to 180° (two right angles).
- Angles **at a point** add up to 360° (four right angles).

Calculate the size of each of the lettered angles, giving reasons for your answers.

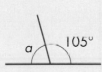

a 105°

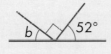

b 52°

160° c

$a = 180° - 105°$ Angles on a straight line add up to
$a = 75°$ 180°.
$b = 180° - (52° + 90°)$ Angles on a straight line add up to
$b = 38°$ 180°.
$c = 360° - (160° + 90°)$ Angles at a point add up to 360°.
$c = 110°$

VERTICALLY OPPOSITE ANGLES

- When two straight lines **intersect** the (vertically) opposite angles are equal.

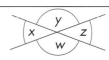

$x = z$
vertically opposite angles
$y = w$
vertically opposite angles

Calculate the size of each of the lettered angles, giving reasons for your answers.

40°
e
d

$d = 40°$ Vertically opposite angles are equal.
$e = 140°$ Angles on a straight line add up to
    180°.

ANGLES BETWEEN PARALLEL LINES

- Never assume that a diagram has been drawn accurately unless it says so.

- A **transversal** is a line that cuts two or more parallel lines.

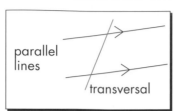

- **Corresponding angles** (or F angles) are equal.

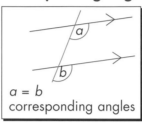

$a = b$
corresponding angles

- **Alternate angles** (or Z angles) are equal.

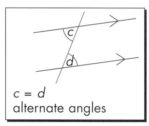 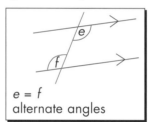

$c = d$
alternate angles

$e = f$
alternate angles

- **Interior angles** add up to 180°.

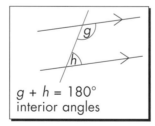

$g + h = 180°$
interior angles

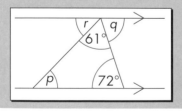

Find the missing angles in this diagram.

From the diagram:

$p = 47°$ The angles of the triangle add up to 180°.

$q = 72°$ Alternate angles between the two parallel lines.

$r = 47°$ Angles on a straight line add up to 180°, or r and p are alternate angles between two parallel lines.

- In questions like this, there are usually several different ways of arriving at the same answer. Trying different methods can serve as a useful check.

ANGLE PROPERTIES
FINAL TEST

CIRCLE PROPERTIES 1

CIRCLE PROPERTIES
PRE-TEST

- These are the names of the main parts of a circle.
  You need to learn them.

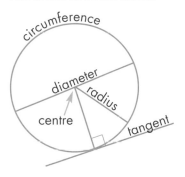

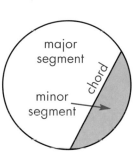

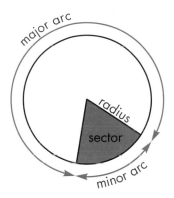

ANGLES AT THE CENTRE AND CIRCUMFERENCE

- The angle **subtended** by an **arc** (or **chord**)
  at the centre is twice that subtended at
  the **circumference** by the same arc.

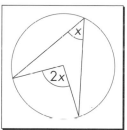

ANGLE SUBTENDED BY THE SAME ARC (CHORD)

- Angles **subtended by the same arc** (or chord) are **equal**.

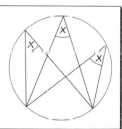

ANGLES OF A CYCLIC QUADRILATERAL

- A **cyclic quadrilateral** is a quadrilateral
  in which all the vertices lie on the **circumference
  of the same circle**.
- The **opposite angles** of a cyclic quadrilateral
  are **supplementary** (i.e. they add up to 180°).

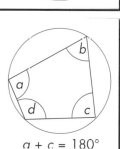

$a + c = 180°$
$b + d = 180°$

In the diagram, O is the centre of the circle. Calculate a and b.
From the diagram:

$a = 55°$ As the angle at the centre is twice the angle
                      at the circumference.

$b = 180° - 55°$ As opposite angles of a cyclic quadrilateral
$b = 125°$ are supplementary.

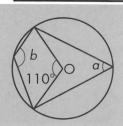

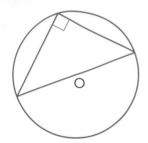

CIRCLE PROPERTIES 2

ANGLES IN A SEMICIRCLE

- The angle in a semicircle is the **angle subtended at the circumference** by a **diameter** of the circle.
- The angle in a semicircle is **always 90°**.

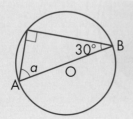

The line AB passes through the centre of the circle.
Calculate the value of a.
As the line AB passes through the centre, it is a diameter.
The angle subtended at the circumference is 90°.

$90° + 30° + a = 180°$ As the angles in a triangle add up
$a = 60°$ to 180°.

... HINT ...

- **In the diagram, OX is the perpendicular bisector of the chord AB, O is the centre of the circle and r is the radius.**

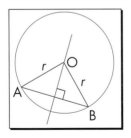

PERPENDICULAR BISECTOR OF A CHORD

- The **perpendicular bisector** of a chord passes through the centre of the circle.

TANGENTS TO A CIRCLE

- A **tangent** is a line that touches a circle in one place.
- A tangent to a circle is **perpendicular to the radius** at the point of contact.
- Tangents to a circle from a **common external point** are **equal in length**.

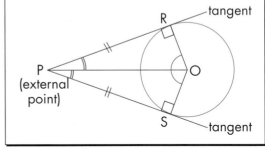

Given that SP and SQ are tangents to the circle, with points of contact at P and Q respectively, find:
a the value of t
b the length QS.

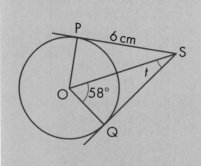

a $t = 180° - 90° - 58°$ As the tangent to a circle is
   $t = 32°$ perpendicular to the radius at the point of contact and the angles in a triangle add up to 180°.

b QS = 6 cm   As tangents to a circle from a common external point are equal in length so SP = SQ.

BEARINGS

- You can use bearings to describe **directions**.
- You can describe bearings in terms of the **points on a compass** or as **angles** or **turns** measured from north in a **clockwise direction**.

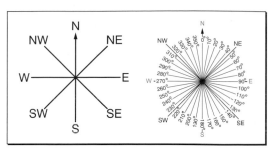

- You usually give bearings as **three-figure numbers**, so a bearing of 55° would usually be written as 055°.
- This table shows how the two ways of describing bearings are related.

Direction	Bearing
North	000°
North-east	045°
East	090°
South-east	135°
South	180°
South-west	225°
West	270°
North-west	315°

The bearing of a ship Q from a rock P is 055°.
What is the bearing of the rock from the ship?

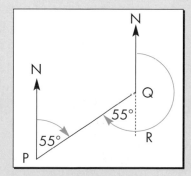

The angle PQR = 55°   Alternate angles between parallel lines.
The bearing of P from Q = 180° + 55°
                        = 235°

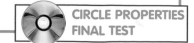

TRANSFORMATIONS PRE-TEST

REFLECTION SYMMETRY

LINE SYMMETRY

- When you can fold a shape so that one half fits exactly over the other half, the shape has **line symmetry** or is **symmetrical**.
- The fold line of a symmetrical shape is called a **line of symmetry**.

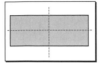

A rectangle has two lines of symmetry.

An equilateral triangle has three lines of symmetry.

This letter H has two lines of symmetry.

This letter N has no lines of symmetry.

PLANE SYMMETRY

- A **plane of symmetry** divides a solid into two equal halves. A cuboid has **three** planes of symmetry.

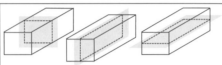

A square-based pyramid has **four** planes of symmetry.

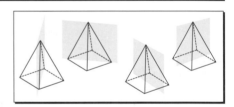

REFLECTION

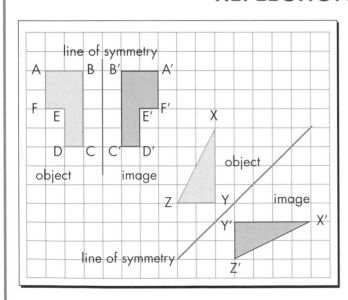

- A **reflection** is a **transformation** in which any two corresponding points on the object and image are the same distance away from a fixed line (called the **line of symmetry** or **mirror line**).
- You can define a reflection by giving the **position** of the line of symmetry.
- You can use tracing paper or a mirror to help you with this work.

ROTATIONAL SYMMETRY

... HINT ...

- **Use tracing paper or a mirror to help you with this work.**

- When you can rotate a shape about its centre to fit exactly over its original position, the shape has **rotational symmetry**.

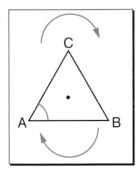

Original position

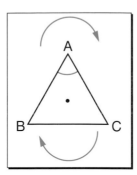

First position – the shape in this position looks identical to the original.

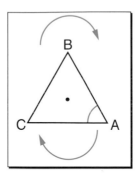

Second position – the shape in this position looks identical to the original.

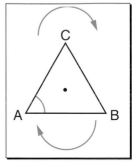

Third position – the shape in this position looks identical to the original and is now back in its starting position.

- The number of different positions in which the shape can be placed is the **order of rotational symmetry**.
  An equilateral triangle has **rotational symmetry of order 3**.

ROTATION

- A **rotation** is a **transformation** in which lines joining any two corresponding points on the object and image make the same angle at a fixed point (called the **centre of rotation**).

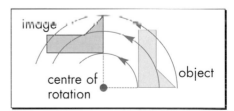

- You can define a rotation by giving the position of the centre of rotation, with the **angle** and the **direction** of the rotation.
- To find the centre of rotation, you need to join corresponding points on the object and image with straight lines and draw the perpendicular bisectors of these lines. The centre of rotation is at the **intersection** of these straight lines.

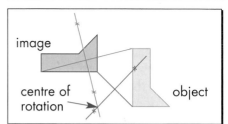

- To find the **angle of rotation**, you need to join corresponding points on the object and image to the centre of rotation. The angle between these lines is the angle of rotation.
- In mathematics an **anticlockwise** turn is described as **positive** (+ve) and a **clockwise** turn is described as **negative** (–ve).

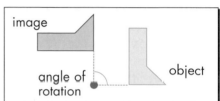

ENLARGEMENT

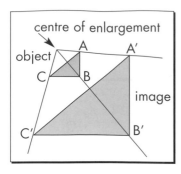

- An **enlargement** is a **transformation** in which the distance between a point on the image and a fixed point (called the **centre of enlargement**) is a **factor** of the distance between the corresponding point on the object and the fixed point.
- You can define an enlargement by giving the position of the centre of enlargement, with the factor of enlargement (called the **scale factor**).
- To find the centre of enlargement, you need to join corresponding points on the object and the image, with straight lines. The centre of enlargement is at the intersection of these straight lines.
- You can find the scale factor (SF) of an enlargement as:

$$SF = \frac{\text{distance of point on image from centre}}{\text{distance of corresponding point on object from centre}}$$

or

$$SF = \frac{\text{distance between two points on image}}{\text{distance between corresponding points on object}}$$

The points A(3, 8), B(7, 8), C(7, ⁻4) and D(3, ⁻2) are joined to form a trapezium which is enlarged, scale factor $\frac{1}{2}$, with (⁻5, ⁻6) as the centre.

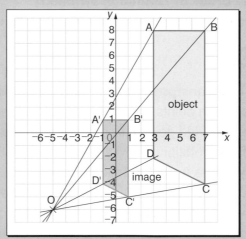

OA = 16.12	OC = 12.2
OA′ = $\frac{1}{2}$ × 16.12	OC′ = $\frac{1}{2}$ × 12.2
= 8.06	= 6.1
OB = 18.44	OD = 8.94
OB′ = $\frac{1}{2}$ × 18.44	OD′ = $\frac{1}{2}$ × 8.94
= 9.22	= 4.47

... HINT ...

- Notice that an enlargement may produce an image that is smaller than the object. This happens when the scale factor is smaller than 1.

TRANSLATION

- A **translation** is a **transformation** in which the distance and direction between any two corresponding points on the object and image are the same.
- You can define a translation by giving the **distance** and **direction** of the translation.

A This is a translation of six units to the right.

B This is a translation of seven units right and four units up.

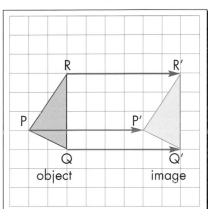

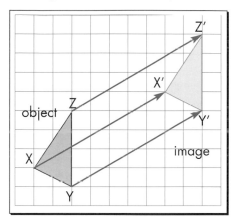

- You can use **vector notation** to describe translations.

The notation is written as: $\begin{pmatrix} \text{units moved in } x\text{-direction} \\ \text{units moved in } y\text{-direction} \end{pmatrix}$

so translation A (above) can be written as $\binom{6}{0}$ and

translation B (above) can be written as $\binom{7}{4}$.

The triangle ABC with coordinates A(1, 1), B(3, 2) and C(2, 5) undergoes a translation of $\binom{2}{-6}$ to A'B'C'. Show the triangles ABC and A'B'C' and write down the translation that will return A'B'C' to ABC.

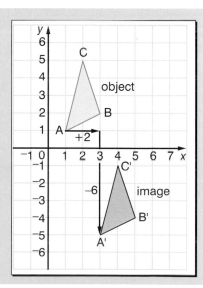

The vector $\binom{2}{-6}$ is a movement of 2 units to the right and
-6 units upwards
(i.e. 6 units downwards).

The translation that will return A'B'C' to ABC is $\binom{-2}{6}$.

COMBINING TRANSFORMATIONS

... HINT ...

- You can see from the example below that the order of the transformations is important.

- When one translation is followed by another, the result is a **combined transformation**.
- Sometimes a combination of the same type of transformation or a combination of different transformations can be described as a **single transformation**.

COMMON ✗ MISTAKE

- If the question asks for a single transformation that is equivalent to a combined transformation, then you must give just the single transformation.

If R is a reflection in the y-axis and T is a rotation of $^-90°$ about the origin, show (on separate diagrams) the image of the triangle XYZ with vertices X(2, 1), Y(2, 5) and Z(4, 2) under these combined transformations.

a T followed by R   b R followed by T.

In each case, write down the single transformation that will return the image formed by the combined transformations to its original position.

a

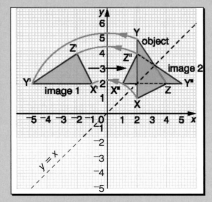

The single transformation that will return X'Y'Z' to XYZ is a reflection in the line $y = x$.

b

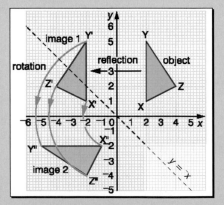

The single transformation that will return X''Y''Z'' to XYZ is a reflection in the line $y = ^-x$.

TESSELLATIONS

- If congruent shapes fit together exactly, with no gaps, to cover an area completely, then the shapes **tessellate**.
- These shapes tessellate.

- These are examples of shapes that **do not** tessellate.

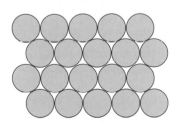

Study these shapes. Say which ones will tessellate and which will not.

a   b   c   d

e   f   g

Shapes a, b, c, e, f and g will tessellate.

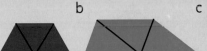

a   b   c

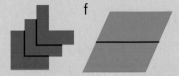 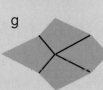

e   f   g

Shape d is a regular pentagon.
Regular pentagons do not tessellate as the angles at their vertices cannot be placed together to form a total of 360° with no gaps.

Gap here means that regular pentagons cannot tessellate

TRANSFORMATIONS
FINAL TEST

POLYGONS
PRE-TEST

• • • HINT • • •

- **You should know that 'tri' means 'three', so words that include 'tri' often relate to things that have three parts.**

COMMON X MISTAKE

- **Look out for special triangles where you might not expect them! Radii of a circle are always equal so don't miss out on isosceles triangles.**

TRIANGLES

- A **triangle** is a plane shape with three straight sides.

EQUILATERAL TRIANGLES

- A **regular** triangle, in which all three sides are the same and all three angles are the same, is called an **equilateral** triangle. Each angle is 60° (180° ÷ 3 = 60°).
- An equilateral triangle has **three lines of reflection symmetry** and **rotational symmetry of order 3**.

ISOSCELES TRIANGLES

- A triangle with two equal sides is called an **isosceles** triangle.
- In an isosceles triangle, the angles opposite the equal sides are equal.
- An isosceles triangle has **one line of symmetry**.

RIGHT-ANGLED TRIANGLES

- A triangle in which **one angle is 90°** is a right-angled triangle.

- It is possible for a triangle to be right-angled and **isosceles**.

ACUTE-ANGLED TRIANGLES

- A triangle in which all of the angles are acute is an acute-angled triangle (see page 58).

OBTUSE-ANGLED TRIANGLES

- A triangle in which one of the angles is obtuse is an obtuse-angled triangle (see page 58).

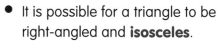

QUADRILATERALS

- A **quadrilateral** is a plane shape with four sides.
- You can divide any quadrilateral into **two triangles** by joining opposite corners, then you can show that the angles of a quadrilateral add up to 360°.

SQUARES

- A **regular** quadrilateral in which all four sides are the same and all four angles are the same is called a **square**. Each angle is 90° (360° ÷ 4 = 90°).
- A square has **four lines of reflection symmetry** and **rotational symmetry of order 4**.

RECTANGLES

- A **rectangle** is a quadrilateral in which opposite sides are equal and all four angles are right angles.
- A rectangle has only two lines of symmetry. The diagonal is **not** a line of symmetry.

RHOMBUSES

- A **rhombus** is a quadrilateral with four equal sides. Its opposite angles are equal. Its diagonals bisect each other at right angles.
- A rhombus is often called a diamond.

PARALLELOGRAMS

- A **parallelogram** is a quadrilateral in which both pairs of opposite sides are equal and parallel.

KITES

- A **kite** is a quadrilateral with two pairs of adjacent sides equal.
- A kite has one line of symmetry.

TRAPEZIUMS (OR TRAPEZIA)

- A **trapezium** is a quadrilateral with one pair of parallel sides.
- There are three types of trapezium. The isosceles trapezium has one line of symmetry.

... HINTS ...

- You should know that 'quad' means 'four', so words that include 'quad' often relate to things with four parts.
- The 'lateral' in quadrilateral means 'side'.

... HINTS ...

- A rhombus is a parallelogram with equal sides.
- A parallelogram is like a rhombus with one pair of opposite sides lengthened.
- There are three types of trapezium. General

Isosceles

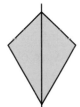

Right-angled

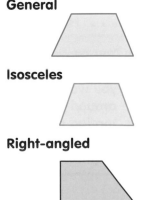

POLYGONS

- Any plain shape enclosed by straight lines is called a **polygon**.
- Polygons get their names from the number of sides.

Number of sides	Name of polygon
3	triangle
4	quadrilateral
5	pentagon
6	hexagon
7	heptagon or septagon
8	octagon
9	nonagon
10	decagon

- In a **regular** polygon, all the sides are equal and all the angles are equal.

Regular hexagon

Irregular hexagon

- A **convex** polygon has no interior angle greater than 180°.
- A **concave** (or **re-entrant**) polygon has at least one interior angle greater than 180°.

180°

EXTERIOR ANGLES OF A POLYGON

- The **exterior angle** of a polygon is formed when a side of the polygon is continued externally.
- The exterior angle and its adjacent **interior angle** add up to 180° (angles on a straight line).
- The **sum** of all the exterior angles of a polygon is 360°.

... HINT ...

- You can convince yourself of this if you walk a pencil around a polygon, turning the pencil though each angle in turn.

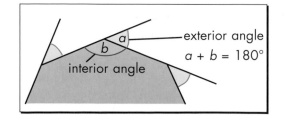

exterior angle

$a + b = 180°$

interior angle

INTERIOR ANGLES OF A POLYGON

- You can find the **sum of the interior angles** of a polygon by drawing diagonals from one **vertex** (or corner) to divide the polygon into triangles. Each triangle has an **angle sum of 180°**.
- A **four-sided polygon** can be split into **two triangles**.
Angle sum = 2 × 180° = 360°

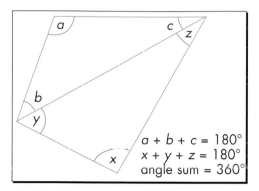

$a + b + c = 180°$
$x + y + z = 180°$
angle sum = 360°

- A **five-sided polygon** can be split into **three triangles**.
Angle sum = 3 × 180° = 540°

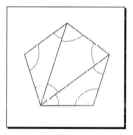

- An **eight-sided polygon** can be split into **six triangles**.
Angle sum = 6 × 180° = 1080°

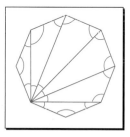

- From these diagrams, you can see that an *n*-sided polygon can be split into (*n* – 2) triangles.
- You can use this **formula** for the angle sum.
The angle sum of an *n*-sided polygon is (*n* – 2) × 180°.

••• HINT •••

- **The angle sum of an *n*-sided polygon can also be written as (2*n* – 4) × 90° or (2*n* – 4) right angles.**

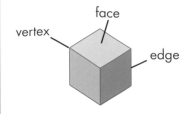

vertex · face · edge

SOLIDS

- A **solid** is a three-dimensional shape such as a cube, cuboid, prism, cylinder, sphere, pyramid or cone.
- A **face** is the surface of a solid which is enclosed by edges.
- An **edge** is a straight line where two faces meet.
- A **vertex** is the point where three or more edges meet.

TYPES OF SOLID

- A **cube** is a three-dimensional shape with six square faces.

- A **cuboid** is a three-dimensional shape with six rectangular faces. Opposite faces are equal in size.

... HINT ...

- **Wherever you cut a prism, perpendicular to its length, the shape of the cut face will always be the same.**

- A **prism** is a three-dimensional shape with uniform cross-section. The prism is usually named after the shape of the cross-sectional area.

Hexagonal prism

Triangular prism

- A **cylinder** is a prism with a uniform circular cross-section.

- A **sphere** is a three-dimensional shape in which every point on the surface is always the same distance from the centre.

Square-based pyramid

- A **pyramid** is a three-dimensional shape with a polygon-shaped base, in which the remaining triangular faces meet at a vertex. The pyramid is usually named after the shape of the polygon forming the base. A **right pyramid** has its vertex vertically above the centre of its base.

- A **cone** is a pyramid with a circular base.

NETS

- A **net** is a pattern that can be cut out and folded to form a 3D shape. These are the most common nets.

Cube

Net for a cube

Cuboid

Net for a cuboid

Triangular prism

Net for a triangular prism

Square-based pyramid

Net for a square-based pyramid

Cylinder

Net for a cylinder

Cone

Net for a cone

POLYGONS
FINAL TEST

MEASUREMENT
PRE-TEST

LENGTH, AREA AND VOLUME 1

- Circumference of a circle = $\pi \times$ diameter
                            = $2 \times \pi \times$ radius
- Area of a circle = $\pi \times$ (radius)^2

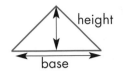

- Area of a triangle
  = $\frac{1}{2} \times$ base $\times$ perpendicular height

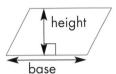

- Area of a parallelogram
  = base $\times$ perpendicular height

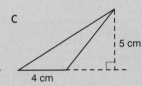

Find the area of each triangle.

a   b   c

5 cm   5 cm   5 cm

3 cm   7 cm   4 cm

a   Area of a triangle = $\frac{1}{2} \times$ base $\times$ perpendicular height

            = $\frac{1}{2} \times 3 \times 5$ Perpendicular height is
                          5 cm.

            = 7.5 cm^2 Remember to include the
                          units of area.

b   Area of a triangle = $\frac{1}{2} \times$ base $\times$ perpendicular height

            = $\frac{1}{2} \times 7 \times 5$ Perpendicular height is
                          5 cm again.
            = 17.5 cm^2

c   Area of a triangle = $\frac{1}{2} \times$ base $\times$ perpendicular height

            = $\frac{1}{2} \times 4 \times 5$ Perpendicular height is
                          still 5 cm.
            = 10 cm^2

Find the area of the parallelogram.

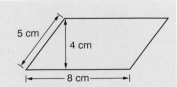

5 cm   4 cm

8 cm

Area of a parallelogram = base $\times$ perpendicular height
                         = 8×4 Perpendicular height is
                         = 32 cm^2 4 cm (not 5 cm).

Find the area of the kite.

To find the area of a kite it is helpful to split the shape into two triangles and use:

area of a triangle = $\frac{1}{2}$ × base × perpendicular height

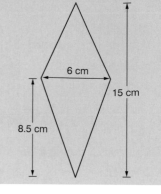

Area of kite
= $\frac{1}{2}$ × 6 × 6.5 + $\frac{1}{2}$ × 6 × 8.5   Height of top triangle
= 19.5 + 25.5   = 15 − 8.5 = 6.5 cm.
= 45 cm^2

- An easier way to find the area of a kite is to multiply the width by the height and divide by 2.

Area of a kite = $\frac{1}{2}$ × width × height

So for the example above, the area of the kite is

$\frac{1}{2}$ × 6 × 15 = 45 cm^2.

• • • HINT • • •

- **Before you use it, you need to know why this works, so look again at the example carefully.**

- You will find it useful to know how to find the area and perimeter of a semicircle.

Area of a semicircle = $\frac{1}{2}$ × π × r^2

Perimeter of a semicircle = $\frac{1}{2}$ × π × d + d

Find the area and the perimeter of a semicircle of diameter 12 metres.

Area of a semicircle = $\frac{1}{2}$ × area of a circle

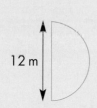

$= \frac{1}{2} \times \pi r^2$ Area of a circle = πr^2

$= \frac{1}{2} \times \pi \times 6^2$ Radius = $\frac{1}{2}$ × diameter

$= \frac{1}{2} \times \pi \times 36 = 18\pi$

$= 39.269\,908$

$= 39.3\,m^2$ (3 s.f.)

Perimeter of a semicircle = $\frac{1}{2}$ × circumference of circle + diameter

Perimeter = $\frac{1}{2} \times 2\pi r + d$ Circumference of a circle = $2\pi r$ and
                                                      diameter = d.

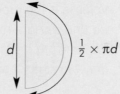

$= \frac{1}{2} \times 2 \times \pi \times 6 + 12$

$= 6\pi + 12$

$= 25.707\,963$

$= 25.7\,m$ (3 s.f.)

• • • HINTS • • •

- **The examination question may ask you to give your answer in terms of π.**
- **Answers of 18π m^2 and 6π + 12 m would be accepted.**

LENGTH, AREA AND VOLUME 2

- Volume of a **cuboid**
  = length × width
  × height

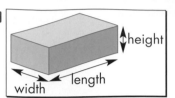

- Area of a **trapezium**
  = $\frac{1}{2}(a + b)h$

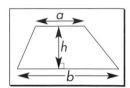

- Volume of a **cylinder**
  = $\pi r^2 h$

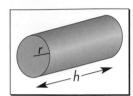

- Volume of a **prism**
  = area of cross-section
  × length

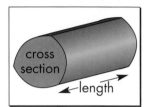

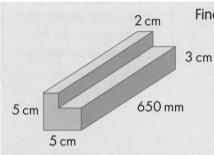

Find the volume of the prism with dimensions as shown.

Volume of a prism = area of cross-section × length
Area of cross-section = 5 × 3 + 2 × 2 = 15 + 4 = 19 cm²
Volume of a prism = area of cross-section × length

     = 19 × 65 Writing all lengths in the same
            units with 10 mm = 1 cm.

     = 1235 cm³
     = 1240 cm³ (3 s.f.)

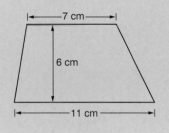

Find the area of the trapezium.

Area of trapezium = $\frac{1}{2}$ × $(a + b)$ × height

      = $\frac{1}{2}$ × (7 + 11) × 6 Perpendicular height
               is 6 cm.

      = $\frac{1}{2}$ × 18 × 6

      = 54 cm²

UNITS FOR LENGTH, AREA AND VOLUME

... HINT ...

- If you ignore constants (including π) you should be able to identify length, area and volume.

- You can identify lengths, areas and volumes by looking at the **formulae** or **units**.
- Area is the product of two lengths.
- Volume is the product of three lengths.
- πd and $2\pi r$ are measures of **length**.
- bh, $(a + b)h$ and πr^2 are measures of **area**.
- lbh, $\frac{4}{3}\pi r^3$, $\pi r^2 h$ and $\frac{1}{2}a^2 h$ are measures of **volume**.

GEOMETRICAL CONSTRUCTIONS

THE PERPENDICULAR BISECTOR OF A LINE (AB)

1 With the **compasses** set to a radius greater than half the length of AB, and **centred on A**, draw arcs **above** and **below** the line.

2 With the compasses still set to the **same radius**, and **centred on B**, draw arcs **above** and **below** the line, **to cut the first arcs**.

3 Join the points where the arcs cross (P and Q). This line is the **perpendicular bisector** of AB.

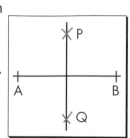

THE PERPENDICULAR FROM A POINT ON A STRAIGHT LINE

1 With the compasses set to a suitable radius, and **centred on the point, X**, draw arcs to cut the line at two points, A and B.

2 Now construct the **perpendicular bisector** of the line segment AB.

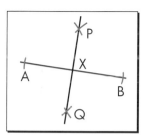

THE PERPENDICULAR FROM A POINT TO A STRAIGHT LINE

1 With compasses set to suitable radius, and **centred on the point, P**, draw arcs to cut the line at two points, A and B.

2 With the compasses set to a radius greater than half the length of AB, and **centred on A**, draw an arc on the **opposite** side of the line from P.

3 With the compasses still set to the **same radius**, and **centred on B**, draw an arc to cut the arc drawn in step 2, at Q.

4 Join PQ.

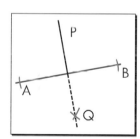

THE ANGLE BISECTOR (OF ∠ABC)

1 With the compasses set to a suitable radius, for example, about 5 cm, and **centred on B**, draw arcs to cut BA at L and BC at M.

2 With the compasses set to the same radius, and **centred on L**, draw an arc between BA and BC.

3 With the compasses set to the same or greater radius, and **centred on M**, draw an arc to cut the arc between BA and BC, at Q.

4 Join BQ. This is the **bisector of angle ABC**.

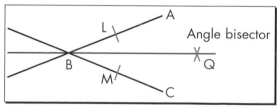

LOCUS OF POINTS

- A **locus** is a path followed by a point that moves to satisfy some given rule.

A POINT MOVING AT A FIXED DISTANCE FROM A POINT O

- The locus of a point moving so that it is a fixed distance from a point O is a **circle** with centre O.

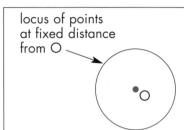

locus of points at fixed distance from O

A POINT MOVING AT A FIXED DISTANCE FROM TWO FIXED POINTS A AND B

- The locus of a point moving so that it is a fixed distance from two fixed points, A and B, is the **perpendicular bisector** of the line AB.

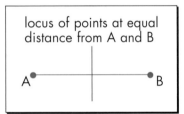

locus of points at equal distance from A and B

A POINT MOVING AT A FIXED DISTANCE FROM THE LINE PQ

- The locus of a point moving so that it is a fixed distance from the line PQ is a **pair of lines parallel to PQ**, one on either side of the line, with a semicircle centred at each of the points P and Q.

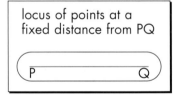

locus of points at a fixed distance from PQ

A POINT MOVING AT A FIXED DISTANCE FROM TWO LINES AB AND CD

- The locus of a point moving so that it is a fixed distance from two lines, AB and CD, is the **pair of bisectors of the angles** between the two lines (drawn from the point where the lines cross).

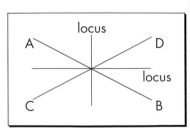

CONGRUENT TRIANGLES

- Two triangles are **congruent** if one of the triangles can be fitted exactly over the other, so that **all corresponding angles** and **all corresponding sides** are equal.
- In the two triangles shown:

  AB = XY $\quad \angle A = \angle X$

  BC = YZ $\quad \angle B = \angle Y$

  CA = ZX $\quad \angle C = \angle Z$

- If the two triangles ABC and XYZ are congruent then you can write DABC ≡ DXYZ.
- These **minimum conditions** are enough to show that two triangles are congruent:
  - two angles and a side of one triangle equal two angles and the corresponding side of the other (**AAS**)
  - two sides and the included angle of one triangle equal two sides and the included angle of the other (**SAS**)
  - the three sides of one triangle equal the three sides of the other (**SSS**).
- If the triangles are right-angled then they are congruent if the hypotenuses are equal and two other corresponding sides are equal in the triangles (**RHS**).

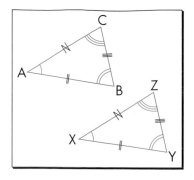

••• HINTS •••

- **Show equal sides by matching dashes or marks, show equal angles by matching arcs as above.**
- **You may need to turn one of the triangles over to fit over the other one, but this still counts as being congruent.**

SIMILAR TRIANGLES

- Two triangles are **similar** if one of the triangles is an **enlargement** of the other triangle.
- In similar triangles, all corresponding angles are equal and corresponding sides are in the **same ratio**.

  $\angle A = \angle X$

  $\angle B = \angle Y$

  $\angle C = \angle Z$

- If two triangles are similar then the **ratios of the corresponding sides are equal**.

  $$\frac{AB}{XY} = \frac{BC}{YZ} = \frac{CA}{ZX} \quad \text{or} \quad \frac{XY}{AB} = \frac{YZ}{BC} = \frac{ZX}{CA}$$

- These **minimum conditions** are enough to show that two triangles are similar:
  - two angles of one triangle equal two angles of the other
  - two pairs of sides are in the same ratio and the included angles are equal
  - three pairs of sides are in the same ratio.

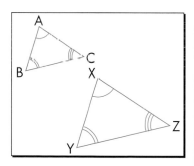

COMMON ✗ MISTAKE

- When you describe similar triangles, the order of the angles is important. Get them right.

MEASUREMENT
FINAL TEST

TRIGONOMETRY
PRE-TEST

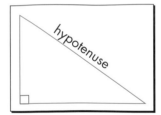

PYTHAGORAS' THEOREM

- In any right-angled triangle, the side opposite the right angle is called the **hypotenuse** and this is always the longest side.
- **Pythagoras' theorem** states that:
  For any right-angled triangle, the square of the length of the hypotenuse is equal to the sum of the squares of the lengths of the other two sides.
- It is usual to **label a triangle** like this.

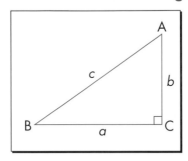

Using Pythagoras' theorem: $a^2 + b^2 = c^2$

... HINT ...

- The answer $\sqrt{34}$ is in surd form. Any expression that involves square roots is called a surd.

Use Pythagoras' theorem to find the missing length of the side in this right-angled triangle.

$$a^2 + b^2 = c^2$$
$$3^2 + 5^2 = c^2$$
$$c^2 = 3^2 + 5^2$$
$$c^2 = 9 + 25$$
$$c^2 = 34$$
$$c = \sqrt{34}\,\text{cm}$$

Leave the answer as $\sqrt{34}$ cm or write it as 5.83 cm (3 s.f.).

... HINTS ...

- On a non-calculator paper you should usually leave your answer in surd form.
- On a calculator paper you should normally round your answers to an appropriate degree of accuracy (e.g. 3 s.f.).

Use Pythagoras' theorem to find the missing length of the side in this right-angled triangle.

$$a^2 + b^2 = c^2$$
$$a^2 + 8^2 = 14^2$$
$$a^2 + 64 = 196$$
$$a^2 = 196 - 64$$
$$a^2 = 132$$
$$a = \sqrt{132}$$

Leave the answer as $\sqrt{132}$ or write it as 11.5 (3 s.f.).

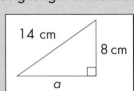

TRIGONOMETRY 1

NAMING ANGLES AND SIDES

- Angles can be labelled in many different ways. For example this angle can be labelled as:

$\angle ABC$, $\angle CBA$, $\angle B$, $A\hat{B}C$, $C\hat{B}A$, $\hat{B}$ or just B.

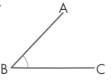

- The sides of a right-angled triangle are given special names, in relation to one of the **acute angles**, as shown in these diagrams.

For angle A:

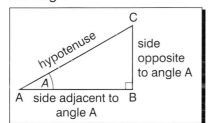

For angle C:

SINE OF AN ANGLE

- The **sine** of an angle (usually abbreviated as **sin**) is the ratio:

$$\frac{\text{length of opposite side}}{\text{length of hypotenuse}}$$

So $\sin A = \dfrac{\text{length of side opposite to } A}{\text{length of hypotenuse}} = \dfrac{BC}{AC}$

and $\sin C = \dfrac{\text{length of side opposite to } C}{\text{length of hypotenuse}} = \dfrac{AB}{AC}$

COSINE OF AN ANGLE

- The **cosine** of an angle (usually abbreviated as **cos**) is the ratio:

$$\frac{\text{length of adjacent side}}{\text{length of hypotenuse}}$$

So $\cos A = \dfrac{\text{length of side adjacent to } A}{\text{length of hypotenuse}} = \dfrac{AB}{AC}$

and $\cos C = \dfrac{\text{length of side adjacent to } C}{\text{length of hypotenuse}} = \dfrac{BC}{AC}$

• • • HINT • • •

- Trigonometry involves using information given in a triangle to find out more information that is not given.

COMMON ✗ MISTAKE

- Make sure your calculator is set to degrees.

• • • HINT • • •

- Make sure you use the correct ratio. Sine is linked with opposite and hypotenuse. Cosine is linked with adjacent and hypotenuse.

COMMON ✗ MISTAKE

- Sines and cosines of angles from 0 to 90° are always between 0 and 1, so if your answer is negative or bigger than 1, it is wrong.

TRIGONOMETRY 2

TANGENT OF AN ANGLE

- The **tangent** of an angle (usually abbreviated as **tan**) is the ratio:

$$\frac{\text{length of opposite side}}{\text{length of adjacent side}}$$

So $\tan A = \dfrac{\text{length of side opposite to } A}{\text{length of side adjacent to } A} = \dfrac{BC}{AB}$

and $\tan C = \dfrac{\text{length of side opposite to } C}{\text{length of side adjacent to } C} = \dfrac{AB}{BC}$

USING SINE, COSINE AND TANGENT TO FIND LENGTHS

- You can use the sine, cosine and tangent ratios to find **missing lengths** in triangles.

Find the length c in this right-angled triangle.

$\cos B = \dfrac{\text{length of adjacent side}}{\text{length of hypotenuse}}$

$\cos 21° = \dfrac{15.8}{c}$

$c \times \cos 21° = 15.8$

$c = \dfrac{15.8}{\cos 21°}$ $\cos 21° = 0.933\,580\,4$

$c = \dfrac{15.8}{0.933\,580\,4} = 16.9 \text{ cm (3 s.f.)}$

Find the area of this rectangle.

Area of rectangle = base × perpendicular height

To find the base, use $\tan A = \dfrac{\text{length of opposite side}}{\text{length of adjacent side}}$

$\tan 28° = \dfrac{18}{\text{base}}$

base $\times \tan 28° = 18$

base $= \dfrac{18}{\tan 28°}$ $\tan 28° = 0.531\,709\,4$

base $= \dfrac{18}{0.531\,709\,4} = 33.853\,076 \text{ cm}$

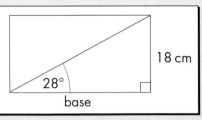

Rounding to an appropriate degree of accuracy and remembering to include the units.

Area of rectangle $= 33.853\,076 \times 18 = 609.355\,37$
$= 609 \text{ cm}^2 \text{ (3 s.f.)}$

USING SINE, COSINE AND TANGENT TO FIND ANGLES

- You can find the angles of a right-angled triangle by using the $\sin^{-1}$ (or arcsin), $\cos^{-1}$ (or arccos) and $\tan^{-1}$ (or arctan) buttons on your calculator.
- First you need to find the sine, cosine or tangent of the angle, then you can use the **inverse button** to find the angle.

Find the angles marked a and b in these right-angled triangles.

a
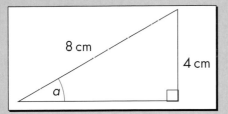

b
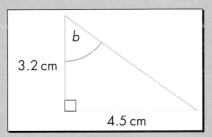

a $\quad \sin a = \dfrac{\text{length of opposite side}}{\text{length of hypotenuse}}$

$\quad \sin a = \dfrac{4}{8}$

$\quad \sin a = 0.5$

$\quad a = \sin^{-1} 0.5$

$\quad a = 30°$

b $\quad \tan b = \dfrac{\text{length of opposite side}}{\text{length of adjacent side}}$

$\quad \tan b = \dfrac{4.5}{3.2}$

$\quad \tan b = 1.406\,25$

$\quad b = \tan^{-1} 1.406\,25$

$\quad b = 54.6°$ (3 s.f.)

... HINTS ...

- Make sure you know which buttons on your calculator will give the trigonometric ratios sine (sin), cosine (cos) and tangent (tan).
- Make sure you know what the inverse ratios are called on your calculator, and how to use them.
- Remember that the smallest angle will always be opposite the smallest side.

COMMON **X** MISTAKE

- If the question says 'Calculate...' then you must calculate, not measure.

ELEVATION AND DEPRESSION

- The **angle of elevation** is the angle up from the horizontal.

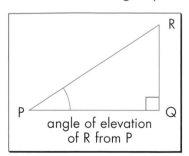

angle of elevation
of R from P

- The **angle of depression** is the angle down from the horizontal.

angle of
depression of
C from A

... HINT ...

- The angle of elevation of the top of a tree from a point on the ground is the same as the angle of depression of the point on the ground from the top of the tree. You should be able to see why.

$x = y$
(alternate angles)

A boat is 40 m away from a cliff. The angle of depression of the boat from the top of the cliff is 35°.

Calculate the height of the cliff.

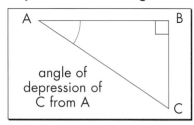

For the right-angled triangle, $\tan 35° = \dfrac{h}{40}$

$h = 40 \tan 35°$
$= 40 \times 0.700\,207\,538$
$= 28.008\,301\,53$
$= 28.0\,\text{m}$ (3 s.f.)

A tree of height 30 feet casts a shadow which is 36 feet long. What is the angle of elevation of the sun?

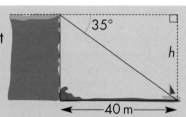

30 feet

36 feet

Let the required angle be θ.

Then $\tan \theta = \dfrac{30}{36} = \dfrac{5}{6} = 0.833\,333\,3\ldots$

$\theta = \tan^{-1} 0.833\,333\,3\ldots = 39.805\,571° = 39.8°$ (3 s.f.)

TRIGONOMETRY
FINAL TEST

COLLECTING AND ORGANISING DATA

REPRESENTING DATA 1 PRE-TEST

COLLECTING DATA

- Any statistical work is based on collecting and organising data to draw conclusions.
- You can collect data in a number of ways although the most popular are **observation**, **interviewing** and the use of **questionnaires**.

CLASSIFYING DATA

- Data that can take **any values** within a given range is called **continuous** data. Heights, temperatures, lengths and mass are examples of continuous data.
- Data that can only take **particular values** (such as whole or half numbers) is called **discrete** data. Numbers of children in families, separate colours and shoe sizes are examples of discrete data.
- **Quantitative data** can only take numerical values. Length, mass, capacity, time and temperature are examples of quantitative data.
- **Qualitative** (or **categorical**) data is more difficult to define, but it includes qualities such as colour, taste, shade or touch.

RAW DATA AND TALLY CHARTS

- **Raw data** is information that has been collected but has not yet been organised in any way.
- You can often use a **tally chart** to collect data. A tally chart consists of a series of tallies grouped into fives, as shown below.

Tallies	Frequency
IIII	= 4
ⅬⅯ	= 5
ⅬⅯ I	= 6
ⅬⅯ II	= 7
ⅬⅯ ⅬⅯ	= 10

- To construct a tally chart, you make one mark or stroke for every item of data counted, but then you draw every fifth stroke through the preceding four. This makes it easy to count how many times each data item occurs, as long as you know your **five-times table** and can **count in fives**.
- The **frequency** of an item of data is the number or times (or **how often** or frequently) it occurs.

QUESTIONNAIRES AND SURVEYS

PRIMARY AND SECONDARY DATA

- **Primary** data is information that you collect as part of a statistical investigation such as a census or survey, but **secondary** data is information that already exists, such as national census figures.
- Once you have collected and processed primary data, it becomes secondary data. Examples include information from government departments, businesses and market research companies.

OBSERVATION

- Observation is the process of **collecting information** and using some suitable method to **record** it, such as observation sheets, tape recorders or video recorders.
- This form of data collection can include **systematic observation**, where you, as the observer, try to be as unobtrusive as possible, or **participant observation**, where you, as the observer, participate in the activity.

INTERVIEWING

- To do this you need to use some **set format** to ask questions of individuals, or groups of individuals.
- If your interviewing is to be **formal**, your questions will follow a strict format. If it is to be **informal**, your questions will follow some general format.

... HINTS ...

- Your questionnaire should be simple, short, clear and precise.
- The questions should be unbiased and unambiguous, written in appropriate language, avoiding personal or offensive questions.

QUESTIONNAIRES

- This is the most popular method of collecting data. It usually involves postal questionnaires or questionnaires that you can leave for the respondents to complete in their own time.

PILOT SURVEY

- A pilot survey is an **initial survey** carried out on a small number of people.
- The pilot survey is useful to check for likely problems and show up areas or topics that may need further clarification before the **actual survey** is carried out.

PICTOGRAMS

CHOOSING A WAY TO REPRESENT DATA

- The method that you choose to **display** your data should always be the one that you think is the best to represent the information.
- After you have drawn your diagram, it is important that other people will be able to **interpret** it.
- Remember that you can represent your data in different ways to give different explanations or interpretations of what you have found out.

• • • HINT • • •

- These various interpretations will be particularly useful for your coursework in handling data.

USING PICTOGRAMS

- A pictogram (or **pictograph** or **ideograph**) is a simple way of representing data.
- The **frequency** is how often an item of data occurs. It is shown by the number of identical pictures.
- When you draw a pictogram, you must always give the diagram a **title** and include a **key** to explain what the symbols or pictures represent.
- In a pictogram, you usually choose a **symbol** or **picture** that represents the data clearly.

  You might use  for books

  for cars

  You could also let stand for two books so that stands for one book.

The table shows sales of ice cream in one hour at a seaside kiosk. Show the information as a pictogram.

Ice cream sales				
Flavour	vanilla	strawberry	raspberry	other
Sales	8	4	5	3

Ice cream sales

Vanilla ❧❧❧❧❧❧❧❧

Strawberry ❧❧❧❧

Raspberry ❧❧❧❧❧

Other ❧❧❧

❧ = 1 ice cream

or

Ice cream sales

Vanilla ❧❧❧❧

Strawberry ❧❧

Raspberry ❧❧❦

Other ❦

❧ = 2 ice creams

BAR CHARTS

- Bar charts are another common way of representing data. The **frequencies** of the data are shown as vertical or horizontal **bars of equal width**.
- When you draw a bar chart, you should label the **axes** clearly and give the diagram a **title** to explain what it represents.

Show this information as a bar chart.

Drinks served				
Drink	tea	coffee	milkshake	other
Sales	7	3	4	2

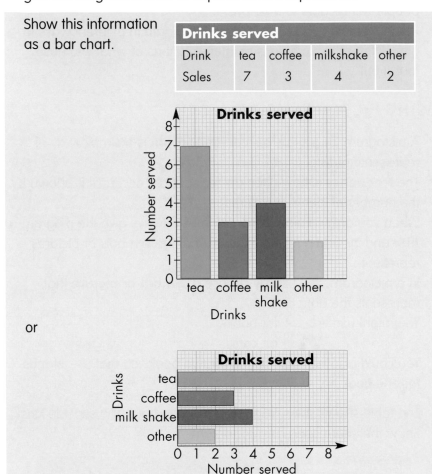

or

- You should be able to **answer questions** about a bar chart.

Look at the bar charts above and use them to answer these questions.
a Which drink is most popular?
b How many milkshakes were served?
c How many drinks altogether were served?

a Tea   This is the highest (or longest) bar.
b 4   Reading from the graph.
c $7 + 3 + 4 + 2 = 16$ Reading from the graph.

REPRESENTING
DATA 1
FINAL TEST

LINE GRAPHS

REPRESENTING
DATA 2
PRE-TEST

- On a line graph, you plot the **frequencies** at various points and join them by a series of **straight lines**.
- You must **label the axes** clearly and give the diagram a **title** to explain what it represents.

Show this information as a line graph.

A patient's temperature						
Time	07.00	08.00	09.00	10.00	11.00	12.00
Temperature (°F)	102.8	101.5	100.2	99.0	98.8	98.6

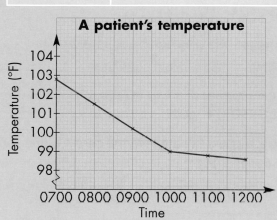

... **HINT** ...

- **Use a ruler to draw straight lines.**

This graph shows the temperatures in Eastbourne during one week in summer.

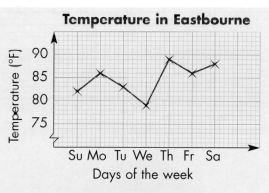

a On which day was the temperature the highest?
b On which day was the temperature the lowest?
c Which two days had the same temperature?

a Thursday (89°F)
b Wednesday (79°F)
c Monday and Friday (both 86°F)

PIE CHARTS

- In a pie chart, the **frequency** of the data is represented by the **angles** (or areas) of the **sectors** of a circle.
- When you draw a pie chart, you must **label** each of the sectors clearly and give the diagram a **title** to explain what it represents.

Show the following information as a pie chart.

Travelling to work				
Travel	bus	walk	cycle	car
Number	36	20	11	23

As there are 90 people, the pie chart must be drawn to represent 90 people.

There are 360° at the centre of a full circle so each person will be shown by 360° ÷ 90 = 4° of the pie chart.

As 36 people travel by bus, the angle at the centre of the sector for 'bus' will be 36 × 4° = 144°.

The table shows the working for all the angles.

Travel	Number	Angle
Bus	36	36 × 4° = 144°
Walk	20	20 × 4° = 80°
Cycle	11	11 × 4° = 44°
Car	23	23 × 4° = 92°
	Total = 90	Total = 360°

... HINT ...

- It is always a good idea to check that the total of the angles is 360°.

Travelling to work

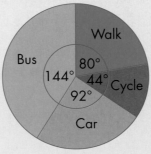

STEM-AND-LEAF DIAGRAMS

- A stem-and-leaf diagram is a useful way to show information.
- It consists of a **stem** and some **leaves** and, together, these illustrate all the data.
- When you use stem-and-leaf diagrams, you must remember to explain the stem (with a **key**) and give your diagram a **title**, to describe what it represents.

The daily numbers of guests in a hotel over a two-week period were recorded. Show this information on a stem-and-leaf diagram. Use the tens-digit as the stem.

```
36   42   42   51   46   32   31
29   27   34   41   43   37   22
```

Number of guests

	2	9	7	2			
	3	6	2	1	4	7	
stem (tens)	4	2	2	6	1	3	leaf (units)
	5	1					

Key: 4 | 2 means 42

- The stem and leaf may also be shown as an **ordered stem-and-leaf diagram**, like this.

Number of guests

	2	2	7	9			
	3	1	2	4	6	7	
stem (tens)	4	1	2	2	3	6	leaf (units)
	5	1					

Key: 4 | 2 means 42

BACK-TO-BACK DIAGRAMS

- You can show two sets of data on one display if you use a **back-to-back stem-and-leaf diagram**.

The data shows the number of words in sentences for two newspapers. Show the data as a stem-and-leaf diagram.

Express						Recorder					
11	23	34	28	15	35	41	23	33	26	31	18
36	38	22	36	17	27	34	36	26	40	37	14

	Express		Recorder	
	7 5 1	1	4 8	
	8 7 3 2	2	3 6 6	
Leaf (units)	8 6 6 5 4	3	1 3 4 6 7	Leaf (units)
		4	0 1	

Stem (tens)

Key: 6 | 3 means 36   Key: 3 | 6 means 36

REPRESENTING
DATA 2
FINAL TEST

AVERAGE AND
SPREAD
PRE-TEST

MEASURES OF CENTRAL TENDENCY

- Measures of central tendency are often referred to as averages – **mode**, **median** and **mean**.

MODE

- The mode of a distribution is the **value that occurs most frequently**.

> Find the mode of this distribution.
> 8, 6, 7, 4, 9, 8, 8, 6, 7, 6, 8
> The number 8 occurs most frequently so the mode is 8.

MEDIAN

- The median of a distribution is the **middle value** when you arrange all the values in **numerical order**.

> Find the median of this distribution.
> 8, 6, 7, 4, 9, 8, 8, 6, 7, 6, 8
> Rearranging in numerical order:
> 4, 6, 6, 6, 7, 7, 8, 8, 8, 8, 9
> So the median = 7

- Where there are two middle values (i.e. for an even number of values) you **add the two middle numbers and divide by 2**.

> Find the median of this distribution.
> 8, 6, 7, 4, 9, 8, 8, 6, 7, 6, 8, 10
> Rearranging in order:
> 4, 6, 6, 6, 7, 7, 8, 8, 8, 8, 9, 10
> So the median = (7 + 8) ÷ 2 = 7.5

- In general, the median is the $\frac{1}{2}(n + 1)$th value in the distribution, where n is the number of values in the distribution.

... HINT ...

- In this case there are 12 values and the median is the $\frac{1}{2}(12 + 1)$th $= 6\frac{1}{2}$th value (indicating that it lies between the 6th and 7th values).

MEAN

- To find the mean of a distribution, **add up all the values** in the distribution and **divide this total by the number of values**.

... HINT ...

- The mean is also known as the arithmetic mean.

> Find the mean of this distribution.
> 8, 6, 7, 4, 9, 8, 8, 6, 7, 6, 8
> $$\text{Mean} = \frac{8 + 6 + 7 + 4 + 9 + 8 + 8 + 6 + 7 + 6 + 8}{11} = \frac{77}{11} = 7$$

FREQUENCY DISTRIBUTIONS

- A frequency distribution is a **collection of data for which the frequencies have been given**.

MODE OF A FREQUENCY DISTRIBUTION

- The mode of a frequency distribution is the value that occurs most frequently.

Find the mode of this frequency distribution.

Value	Frequency
4	1
5	0
6	3
7	2
8	4
9	1

The mode of the frequency distribution is 8.

MEDIAN OF A FREQUENCY DISTRIBUTION

- The median of a frequency distribution is the **middle value** when you have arranged **all the values in numerical order**.

Find the median of each of these distributions.

a 8, 6, 7, 4, 9, 8, 8, 6, 7, 6, 8

b 8, 6, 7, 4, 9, 8, 8, 6, 7, 6, 8, 10

a For the distribution:　　8, 6, 7, 4, 9, 8, 8, 6, 7, 6, 8

Rearrange in order:　　4, 6, 6, 6, 7, 7, 8, 8, 8, 8, 9

The median position is given by $\frac{1}{2}(n + 1) = \frac{1}{2}(11 + 1) = $ 6th value.

4, 6, 6, 6, 7, 7, 8, 8, 8, 8, 9

　　　　　↑

So the median is 7.

b For the distribution:　　8, 6, 7, 4, 9, 8, 8, 6, 7, 6, 8, 10

Rearrange in order:　　4, 6, 6, 6, 7, 7, 8, 8, 8, 8, 9, 10

The median position is given by $\frac{1}{2}(n + 1) = \frac{1}{2}(12 + 1) = 6\frac{1}{2}$th value

(i.e. between the 6th and 7th values).

4, 6, 6, 6, 7, 7, 8, 8, 8, 8, 9, 10

　　　　↑

So the median is $\frac{1}{2}(7 + 8) = 7\frac{1}{2}$.

• • • **HINT** • • •

- **You can find the median of a frequency distribution or a grouped frequency distribution from a cumulative frequency diagram (see page 99).**

MEAN OF A FREQUENCY DISTRIBUTION

- You can find the mean of a frequency distribution by **adding up the values of the distribution** and **dividing by the number of values**.

Find the mean of this frequency distribution.

Value	5	6	7	8
Frequency	1	3	2	4

Writing out the values in full:
5, 6, 6, 6, 7, 7, 8, 8, 8, 8
So the mean is:

$$\frac{5 + 6 + 6 + 6 + 7 + 7 + 8 + 8 + 8 + 8}{10} = \frac{69}{10} = 6.9$$

- Alternatively, it may be easier to use this **formula**.

$$\text{mean} = \frac{\Sigma(\text{frequency} \times \text{values})}{\Sigma(\text{frequencies})} = \frac{\Sigma fx}{\Sigma f}$$

where Σ means 'the sum of' and Σf means the number of values.

Find the mean of this frequency distribution.

Value	5	6	7	8
Frequency	1	3	2	4

Value	Frequency	Frequency × value
x	f	fx
5	1	$1 \times 5 = 5$
6	3	$3 \times 6 = 18$
7	2	$2 \times 7 = 14$
8	4	$4 \times 8 = 32$
	$\Sigma f = 10$	$\Sigma fx = 69$

$$\text{Mean} = \frac{\Sigma(\text{frequency} \times \text{values})}{\Sigma(\text{frequencies})} = \frac{\Sigma fx}{\Sigma f}$$
$$= \frac{69}{10}$$
$$= 6.9$$

... HINT ...

- **Make sure your answer is realistic.**

MEAN OF A GROUPED FREQUENCY DISTRIBUTION

- You can't find the exact mean of a grouped frequency distribution, but you can find an **estimate**.
- For a grouped frequency distribution, you use the **mid-interval values** (or midpoints) as 'estimates' of the intervals.
- You can find the mid-interval value by taking the mean of the upper and lower **class boundaries**.
- You can find the mean of a grouped frequency distribution in the same way as for a frequency distribution, by using the mid-interval values (or midpoints) as representative of the interval.

COMMON X MISTAKES

- The mid-interval values are used as estimates for the intervals, so the answer will be an estimate, not an exact value.
- Don't guess the mid-interval value. Take the mean of the upper and lower class boundaries.

This table shows the heights of trees growing in a nursery. Calculate an estimate of the mean height of the trees.

Height (cm)	15–20	20–30	30–40	40–50	50–60	60–70	70–80
Frequency	8	4	5	11	17	2	1

Draw up a new table.

Height	Mid-interval value x	Frequency f	Frequency × mid-interval value fx
15–20	17.5	8	$8 \times 17.5 = 140$
20–30	25	4	$4 \times 25 = 100$
30–40	35	5	$5 \times 35 = 175$
40–50	45	11	$11 \times 45 = 495$
50–60	55	17	$17 \times 55 = 935$
60–70	65	2	$2 \times 65 = 130$
70–80	75	1	$1 \times 75 = 75$
		$\Sigma f = 48$	$\Sigma fx = 2050$

For the grouped frequency distribution:

$$\text{mean} = \frac{\Sigma fx}{\Sigma f}$$

$$= \frac{2050}{48}$$

$$= 42.708\,333\,3$$

$$= 43\,\text{cm to an appropriate degree of accuracy.}$$

• • • HINT • • •

- An answer of 43 cm is appropriate bearing in mind the accuracy of the original data and the inaccuracies resulting from the use of the mid-interval values as an estimate of the particular interval.

MEASURES OF SPREAD

- Measures of spread are useful for comparing data. They tell how spread out, or **consistent**, the data is.

RANGE

- The **range** of a distribution is the numerical difference between the greatest value and least value.
- The range should always be given as a **single value**.

> Find the range of these test marks.
> 9   7   8   10   9   8   8   2   9   10   8
> Rearranging in order:
> 2   7   8   8   8   8   9   9   9   10   10
> Greatest value = 10
> Least value = 2
> Range = greatest value – least value
>   = 10 – 2
>   = 8

INTERQUARTILE RANGE

- While the range can be affected by **extreme values**, the interquartile range only takes the **middle 50% of the distribution** into account.
- You can find the interquartile range by dividing the data into four parts and working out the difference between the **upper quartile** and the **lower quartile**.

> Find the interquartile range of these test marks.
> 9   7   8   10   9   8   8   2   9   10   8
> Arrange the data in order and consider the middle 50% of the distribution.
>
> 2   7   8   8   8   8   9   9   9   10   10
>   ↑   ↑   ↑
>   LQ   median   UQ
>
> Lower quartile = 8
> Upper quartile = 9
> Interquartile range = upper quartile – lower quartile
>   = 9 – 8
>   = 1

AVERAGE AND
SPREAD
FINAL TEST

CUMULATIVE FREQUENCY DIAGRAMS

CUMULATIVE FREQUENCY PRE-TEST

- You can use the cumulative frequency diagram (or *ogive*) to find the median and *quartiles* of a distribution.
- To find the cumulative frequency, find the *accumulated totals* and plot them against the *data values*.
- You can draw the cumulative frequency diagram by joining the points with a *smooth curve*.

The table shows the times (given to the nearest minute) for which customers have to wait to be served in a local shoe shop. Plot this information on a cumulative frequency diagram.

Waiting time (minutes)	Frequency
1–3	6
4–6	11
7–9	20
10–12	13
13–15	5

First, complete the cumulative frequency column.

Waiting time (minutes)	Frequency	Cumulative frequency
1–3	6	6
4–6	11	17
7–9	20	37
10–12	13	50
13–15	5	55

The cumulative frequency diagram looks like this.

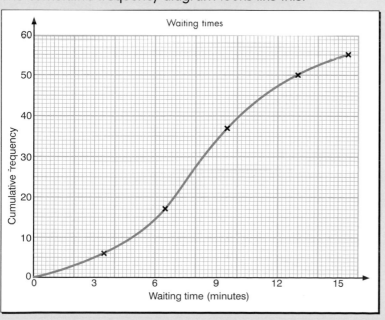

COMMON ✗ MISTAKE

- The cumulative frequency should be the same as the total of all the frequencies. Make sure it is.

● ● ● HINTS ● ● ●

- The final cumulative frequency should equal the sum of the frequencies.
- The cumulative frequencies must always be plotted at the upper class boundaries (i.e. 3.5, 6.5, 9.5, 12.5 and 15.5).
- Remember that the interval of 1–3 minutes, to the nearest minute, includes all values from 0.5 minutes to 3.5 minutes, and so on.

COMMON ✗ MISTAKE

- The points for the cumulative frequency curve must be plotted at the upper class boundaries – the highest values that the data in the interval can take.

USING CUMULATIVE FREQUENCY

- You can use the cumulative frequency diagram to find the **median** and **quartiles** of the given distribution.
- These are shown below, again using the example from page 99.

MEDIAN

- The median is the **middle value** and, in general, the median is the $\frac{1}{2}(n + 1)$th value in the distribution.

- For the cumulative frequency diagram below, the median is given by the $\frac{1}{2}(n + 1)$th value = $\frac{1}{2}(55 + 1)$ = 28th value in the distribution.

INTERQUARTILE RANGE

- The **interquartile range** is the difference between the upper quartile and the lower quartile, where the lower quartile is the $\frac{1}{4}(n + 1)$th value and the upper quartile is the $\frac{3}{4}(n + 1)$th value in the distribution.

- For the cumulative frequency diagram below, the **lower quartile** is given by the $\frac{1}{4}(n + 1) = \frac{1}{4}(55 + 1)$ = 14th value and the **upper quartile** is given by the $\frac{3}{4}(n + 1) = \frac{3}{4}(55 + 1)$ = 42nd value.

From the graph:

median = 8.1   upper quartile = 10.6   lower quartile = 5.9

interquartile range = upper quartile – lower quartile

$$= 10.6 - 5.9 = 4.7$$

> **• • • HINT • • •**
>
> - **Your answers should usually be correct to the nearest half-square (in the example, ±0.1 minutes).**

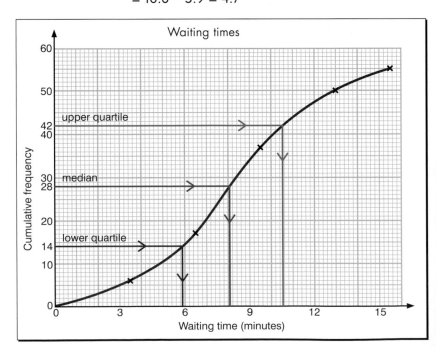

• You can use the cumulative frequency diagram to find out other information about the distribution.

Study the cumulative frequency diagram that shows how long customers waited to be served in the shoe shop.

How many customers waited:

a less than 5 minutes   b more than 10 minutes?

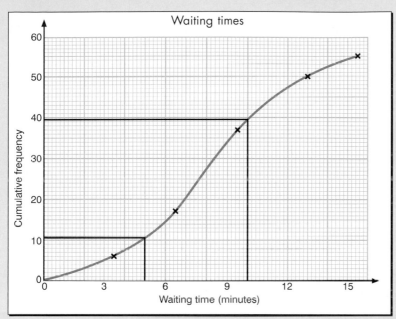

a To find out how many customers waited less than 5 minutes, read the cumulative frequency for a waiting time of 5 minutes From the graph, the number is 10.5.

b To find out how many customers waited more than 10 minutes, read the cumulative frequency for a waiting time of 10 minutes. From the graph, the number of customers who waited less than 10 minutes is 39.5.

So the number of customers who waited more than 10 minutes is 55 − 39.5 = 15.5, or 16 customers to the nearest whole number.

• • •   HINT   • • •

• An answer rounded to 10 or 11 would be acceptable.

COMMON ✗ MISTAKE

• The information that the example above asks for cannot just be read from the table. The 4–6 group includes times up to 6.5 minutes and the 10–12 group includes times from 9.5 minutes to 12.5 minutes.

Waiting time (minutes)	Frequency	Cumulative frequency
1–3	6	6
4–6	11	17
7–9	20	37
10–12	13	50
13–15	5	55

> • Box-and-whisker plots may sometimes be called box-plots.

BOX-AND-WHISKER PLOTS

● A box-and-whisker plot is a diagram that shows:
- the **median**
- the **upper and lower quartiles**
- the **maximum and minimum values**.

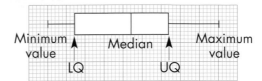

These are the insurance premiums paid by eleven households. Draw a box-and-whisker plot and calculate the interquartile range.

£340 £355 £400 £320 £380 £320 £632
£365 £340 £380 £370

Arrange the data in order.

£320 £320 £340 £340 £355 £365 £370 £380 £380 £400 £632

$\uparrow$ $\uparrow$ $\uparrow$

LQ   Median   UQ

Upper quartile = £380   Lower quartile = £340

Interquartile range = upper quartile − lower quartile
= £380 − £340 = £40

This is the box-and-whisker plot.

● Box plots can be used alongside cumulative frequency graphs to provide information about the **median** and **quartiles** of a distribution more clearly.

Draw a box-and-whisker plot from this graph of waiting times in the shoe shop.

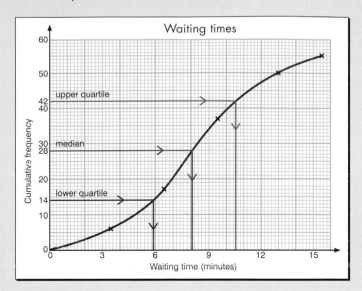

From the graph:
median = 8.1
upper quartile = 10.6
lower quartile = 5.9

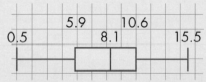

- You can use a box-and-whisker plot to compare **different distributions**.

Here is the box-and-whisker plot for waiting times in the local butcher's shop.
In this case:
median = 9.1   upper quartile = 10.6   lower quartile = 7.9
minimum value = 0.5   maximum value = 15.5

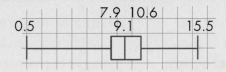

- From the box-and-whisker plots above, you can clearly see that:
  - the range is exactly **the same** for both distributions
  - the median value is **bigger** for the second distribution
  - the spread (of the middle 50%) is **smaller** for the second distribution.

CUMULATIVE
FREQUENCY
FINAL TEST

REPRESENTING
DATA 3
PRE-TEST

SCATTER DIAGRAMS

- You can use **scatter diagrams** (or **scatter graphs**) to show the relationship between two variables.
- You assign each of the two variables to a different axis and then plot the information on the scatter diagram as a series of **coordinates**.

Draw a scatter graph from the information in this table, which shows the heights and shoe sizes of 10 pupils.

Shoe size	3	2	$6\frac{1}{2}$	4	3	6	1	$3\frac{1}{2}$	5
Height (cm)	133	126	158	135	128	152	118	142	150

To draw the scatter graph, consider each pair of values as a pair of coordinates (3, 133), (2, 126), (6, 158), ...

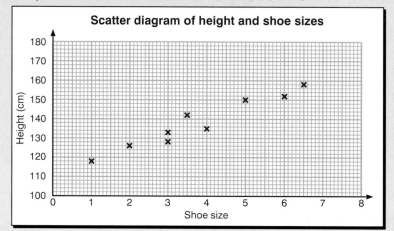

Scatter diagram of height and shoe sizes

CORRELATION

- You can use scatter graphs to show whether there is any relationship or **correlation** between the two variables.

- **Strong correlation**
  Scatter graph to show length against weight of fish

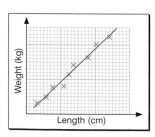

- **Moderate correlation**
  Scatter diagram to show distance travelled against cost per mile

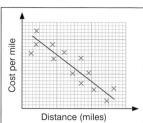

- **Little or no correlation**
  Scatter diagram to show marks in chemistry and art examinations

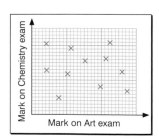

HANDLING DATA

POSITIVE AND NEGATIVE CORRELATION

- Correlation may also be described as **positive** or **negative**.
- If an **increase in one variable** is associated with an **increase in the other variable**, the correlation is positive or **direct**.
    - Scatter diagram to show engine size and maximum speed

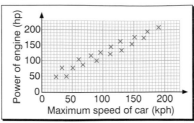

- If an **increase in one variable** is associated with a **decrease in the other variable**, the correlation is negative or **inverse**.
    - Scatter diagram to show thickness of insulation and heat loss

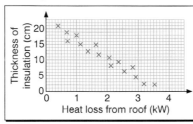

LINES OF BEST FIT

- When the points on a scatter diagram show moderate or strong correlation, you can draw a straight line through, or as close to, as many of the points as possible, to approximate the relationship.
- This is the **line of best fit** (or **regression line**).
- The line of best fit does not necessarily go through the origin.
- You can use the line of best fit to predict other values for the data.

Draw a scatter graph and add the line of best fit for the data in this table, which shows the heights and shoe sizes of 10 pupils.

Shoe size	3	2	$6\frac{1}{2}$	4	3	6	1	$3\frac{1}{2}$	5
Height (cm)	133	126	158	135	128	152	118	142	150

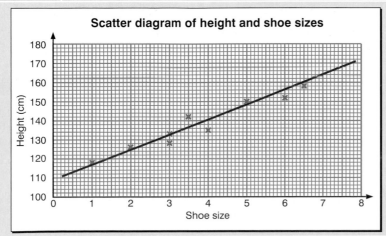

. . . **HINTS** . . .

- **In most cases a line of best fit can be drawn 'by eye'.**
- **There should be as many points above the line as below it.**
- **For accurate work, the line of best fit should pass through $(\bar{x}, \bar{y})$ where $\bar{x}$ and $\bar{y}$ are the mean values of x and y respectively.**

COMMON ✗ MISTAKES

- **The line of best fit does not have to pass through the origin.**
- **You should not try to predict values that are outside the range of the given data.**

TIME SERIES

- The best way to represent data that changes or fluctuates over time is in a **time series graph**.

Year 1	Winter	£55	Year 2	Winter	£63
	Spring	£40		Spring	£48
	Summer	£8		Summer	£16
	Autumn	£25			

The table shows heating costs over two years. Show this data in a graph.

The costs change according to the season but they do not follow a clear pattern or rule, so they cannot be shown on a simple linear graph.

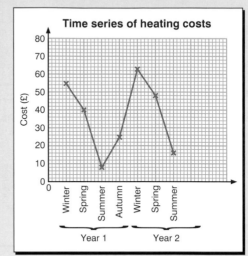

MOVING AVERAGES

- You can also show seasonal trends by using **moving averages**.
- You find a four-point moving average by averaging successive four points at a time.
- Plot the first four-point moving average in the 'middle' of the first four points.

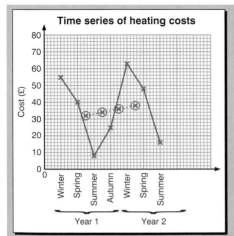

Use moving averages to show the trends in the data in the example above.

The first four-point moving average = $\dfrac{55 + 40 + 8 + 25}{4}$ = £32

The second four-point moving average = $\dfrac{40 + 8 + 25 + 63}{4}$ = £34

The third four-point moving average = $\dfrac{8 + 25 + 63 + 48}{4}$ = £36

The fourth four-point moving average = $\dfrac{25 + 63 + 48 + 16}{4}$ = £38

The four-point moving average can be plotted on the graph as shown.

- The moving average is useful to identify trends. From the graph it is clear that the trend is upwards.

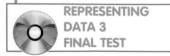

REPRESENTING
DATA 3
FINAL TEST

PROBABILITY 1

PROBABILITY
PRE-TEST

- In probability, an **event** can have several possible **outcomes**.
- An outcome that is **certain** to happen has a probability of 1 whereas an outcome that is **impossible** has a probability of 0.
- In general,

  $$p(\text{success}) = \frac{\text{number of 'successful' outcomes}}{\text{number of possible outcomes}}$$

  where p(success) means 'the probability of success'.

A box contains seven red counters, ten blue counters and eight yellow counters.

- The probability of picking a red counter is:

  $$p(\text{red counter}) = \frac{\text{number of red counters}}{\text{total number of counters}}$$

  $$= \frac{7}{25}$$

- The probability of picking a blue counter is:

  $$p(\text{blue counter}) = \frac{\text{number of blue counters}}{\text{total number of counters}}$$

  $$= \frac{10}{25}$$

  $$= \frac{2}{5} \qquad \text{Cancelling where possible.}$$

- The probability of picking a blue or red counter is:

  p(blue or red counter)

  $$= \frac{\text{number of blue counters + number of red counters}}{\text{total number of counters}}$$

  $$= \frac{10 + 7}{25}$$

  $$= \frac{17}{25}$$

- The probability of picking a green counter is:

  $$p(\text{green counter}) = \frac{\text{number of green counters}}{\text{total number of counters}}$$

  $$= \frac{0}{25}$$

  $$= 0 \qquad \text{i.e. the outcome is impossible.}$$

COMMON ✗ MISTAKE

- If your answer gives a probability greater than 1 or less than 0 it is wrong! Probabilities like this do not have any meaning.

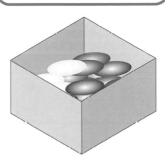

• • • HINT • • •

- You may find it useful to revise addition of fractions and multiplication of fractions.

COMMON ✗ MISTAKE

- You can express a percentage as a fraction, a decimal or a percentage but never as a ratio.

PROBABILITY 2

- The **total of the probabilities** of all the **possible outcomes** for an event is always 1.
- The probability of an outcome **happening** is equal to 1 minus the probability of the outcome **not happening**.

If the probability that it will rain tomorrow is $\frac{1}{3}$, what is the probability that it will not rain tomorrow?
The probability that it will not rain tomorrow is $1 - \frac{1}{3} = \frac{2}{3}$.
i.e. p(not rain) = 1 − p(rain) = $1 - \frac{1}{3} = \frac{2}{3}$

The probability that a bus arrives early is 0.08 and the probability that it arrives on time is 0.63. What is the probability that the same bus arrives late?
p(late) = 1 − p(early or on time)
= 1 − (0.08 + 0.63)
= 1 − 0.71
= 0.29

THEORETICAL AND EXPERIMENTAL PROBABILITY

- Theoretical probability is based on **equally likely outcomes**.
- It is used to predict how an event should perform **in theory**.
- Experimental probability (or **relative frequency**) is used to predict how an event performs **in an experiment**.

This frequency distribution is obtained when a die is thrown 100 times.

Score	1	2	3	4	5	6
Frequency	15	19	18	15	17	16

The theoretical probability of a score of six is $\frac{1}{6}$.
The experimental probability (or relative frequency) of a score of six is $\frac{16}{100} = \frac{4}{25}$ or 0.16.
The expected number of sixes when a die is thrown 100 times is:
$100 \times \frac{1}{6} = 16.6$ or 17 (to the nearest whole number).

POSSIBILITY SPACE DIAGRAMS

- You can use a possibility space diagram to show the different outcomes of **two simultaneous events**.

Two fair dice are thrown and the sum of the scores is noted.
Draw a diagram to illustrate the possible outcomes.

		Second die					
		1	2	3	4	5	6
	1	2	3	4	5	6	7
	2	3	4	5	6	7	8
First die	3	4	5	6	7	8	9
	4	5	6	7	8	9	10
	5	6	7	8	9	10	11
	6	7	8	9	10	11	12

- The diagram in the example above is a possibility space. There are 36 possible outcomes.
- From the diagram:
  - the probability of a sum of 2 is $\frac{1}{36}$

    As there is only one entry with a sum of 2.
  - the probability of a sum of 7 is $\frac{6}{36} = \frac{1}{6}$

    As there are six entries with a sum of 7.
  - the probability of a sum of 10 is $\frac{3}{36} = \frac{1}{12}$

    As there are three entries with a sum of 10.

TREE DIAGRAMS

- A tree diagram is a diagram that shows the probabilities of two or more **different outcomes of events**.
- You write the probabilities of the different outcomes on **different branches**, so that the probabilities on individual pairs (or groups) of branches always add up to 1.

A bag contains five blue and four green discs. A disc is drawn from the bag, it is replaced and then a second disc is drawn from the bag. Draw a tree diagram to show the various possibilities that can occur.

This tree diagram shows the various possibilities that can occur.

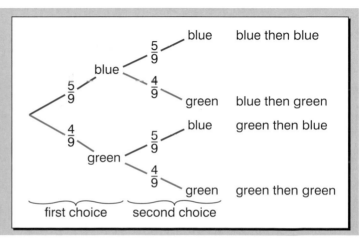

ADDITION RULE FOR MUTUALLY EXCLUSIVE EVENTS

- Outcomes or events are **mutually exclusive** if they cannot both (or all) happen at the same time.
- For mutually exclusive events, you can apply the **addition rule** (also called the **or rule**).

  $p(A \text{ or } B) = p(A) + p(B)$

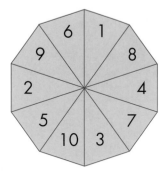

A spinner has ten sides numbered 1 to 10.

- The probability of scoring a five $= p(5) = \frac{1}{10}$

- The probability of scoring a five or a six

  $= p(5 \text{ or } 6) = p(5) + p(6)$ As the events are mutually exclusive.

  $= \frac{1}{10} + \frac{1}{10} = \frac{2}{10} = \frac{1}{5}$ Cancelling to lowest terms.

- The probability of scoring a multiple of 3 or a multiple of 4

  $= p(\text{multiple of 3 or multiple of 4})$

  $= p(\text{multiple of 3}) + p(\text{multiple of 4})$

  As the events are mutually exclusive.

  $= p(3 \text{ or } 6 \text{ or } 9) + p(4 \text{ or } 8)$

  $= p(3) + p(6) + p(9) + p(4) + p(8)$

  As the events are mutually exclusive.

  $= \frac{1}{10} + \frac{1}{10} + \frac{1}{10} + \frac{1}{10} + \frac{1}{10} = \frac{5}{10} = \frac{1}{2}$

- The probability of scoring a multiple of 2 or a multiple of 3

  $= p(\text{multiple of 2 or multiple of 3})$

  These events are not mutually exclusive as the number 6 is common to both events and if the probabilities are added then p(6) will be added twice.

  So p(multiple of 2 or multiple of 3)

  $= p(2 \text{ or } 3 \text{ or } 4 \text{ or } 6 \text{ or } 8 \text{ or } 9 \text{ or } 10)$

  $= p(2) + p(3) + p(4) + p(6) + p(8) + p(9) + p(10)$

  All of these events are now mutually exclusive.

  $= \frac{1}{10} + \frac{1}{10} + \frac{1}{10} + \frac{1}{10} + \frac{1}{10} + \frac{1}{10} + \frac{1}{10}$

  $= \frac{7}{10}$

MULTIPLICATION RULE FOR INDEPENDENT EVENTS

- Outcomes or events are **independent** if one can occur without affecting the others.
- For independent events, you can use the **multiplication rule** (also called the **and rule**).

  p(A and B) = p(A) × p(B)

A bag contains four red counters and three blue counters.
A counter is drawn from the bag, it is replaced and then a second counter is drawn from the bag. Draw a tree diagram to illustrate this situation.

- The probability that both counters will be red = p(red and red)

  = p(red) × p(red) As the events are independent.

  = $\frac{4}{7} \times \frac{4}{7} = \frac{16}{49}$ As the events are independent.

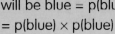

```
                                          4
                                          7 ────── red
                              red ───────
                      4              3
                      7              7 ────── blue
            ──────────
                      3              4
                      7              7 ────── red
                              blue ──────
                                          3
                                          7 ────── blue
            └──────────────────┘ └──────────────────┘
                  1st counter          2nd counter
```

- The probability that both counters will be blue = p(blue and blue)

  = p(blue) × p(blue)   As the events are independent.

  = $\frac{3}{7} \times \frac{3}{7} = \frac{9}{49}$

- The probability that the first counter will be red and the second counter will be blue

  = p(red and blue)

  = p(red) × p(blue)   As the events are independent.

  = $\frac{4}{7} \times \frac{3}{7} = \frac{12}{49}$

- The probability that one counter will be red and one counter will be blue is not the same as the last example.

  No order is specified, so you must find the probability that the first counter will be red and the second counter will be blue **or** the first counter will be blue and the second counter will be red.

  = p(red and blue or blue and red)

  = p(red and blue) + p(blue and red)   As the events are mutually exclusive.

  = p(red) × p(blue) + p(blue) × p(red)   As the events are independent.

  = $\frac{4}{7} \times \frac{3}{7} + \frac{3}{7} \times \frac{4}{7}$

  = $\frac{12}{49} + \frac{12}{49}$

  = $\frac{24}{49}$

PROBABILITY
FINAL TEST

NON-CALCULATOR PAPER

These sample questions are similar to those you may meet in your GCSE examination. Try answering the questions. When you have finished, compare your answers with those given on pages 122–123 to see how well you have done.

Answer all the questions. Do not use a calculator.

1 **a** Work these out.
    (i) 2^5

    (ii) 3^3

   b Write down the next two terms in this sequence.
   23, 16, 9, –, –

   (4 marks)

2 The population of the Earth is approximately 5×10^9 and the Earth's surface area is approximately 4×10^{11} km².
   Calculate the approximate area, in km², per head of population.
   Give your answer in standard form.

   (3 marks)

3 There are blue, red and green discs in a bag.
   A disc is picked at random.
   The probability that the disc is blue is 0.4.
   The probability the disc is red is 0.5.

   a What is the probability of picking a green disc?

   b There are 50 discs in the bag.
   Work out how many of them are blue.

   (3 marks)

4 Using a clean sheet of plain paper, draw the net of this prism accurately.

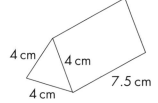

   (3 marks)

5 These are the lengths of paragraphs (in words) of two articles.

Article A	32	43	38	39	50	50	39	45	47	51	36	41	43	44	45	44	47	49
Article B	42	36	37	31	41	30	38	39	46	42	38	33	28	29	34	36	40	41

a Show this information as a stem-and-leaf diagram.

b What do you notice about the two sets of data?

(3 marks)

6 The equation of the straight line $y = mx + c$ is satisfied at the points $(3, 5)$ and $(1, ^-1)$. What is the equation of the straight line?

(2 marks)

7 Solve these inequalities.
a $4x - 3 < 9$

b $11 + 2x > 5x - 5$

(3 marks)

8 a Find the value of 36 multiplied by the reciprocal of 36.
Show your working to explain your answer.

b Carol says, 'The square root of a number is always smaller than the number itself.'
Is she correct?
Give an example to explain your answer.

(4 marks)

9 a Express 36 as a product of its prime factors.

b Find the highest common factor (HCF) of 36 and 60.

(2 marks)

10 Factorise fully the expression $2\pi r^2 + 2\pi rh$.

(3 marks)

11 The diameter of a cylinder is 12 cm and the cylinder is 10 cm high.
Calculate the volume of the cylinder, giving your answer in terms of π.

(3 marks)

12 A rectangle measures 14 cm by 8 cm.
A similar rectangle has sides of length 4 cm and x cm.
What are the possible values of x?

(3 marks)

13 Penny has written down this formula.

$$\text{Volume} = \frac{2}{3}\pi r^4$$

Explain how you can tell that Penny has made a mistake.

(2 marks)

14 This table shows the cumulative frequency for the test results of 72 pupils.

Age group (years)	< 10	10–	20–	30–	40–50
Frequency	6	13	14	23	

From the table calculate:
a how many pupils had marks that were less than or equal to 20

b how many pupils had at least 40 marks.

On a clean sheet of graph paper, draw the cumulative frequency curve for the data. Use your graph to calculate:
c the median and the interquartile range.

In the next test, also marked out of 50, the interquartile range was 30.
d Use the interquartile ranges to comment on the results of the two tests.

(6 marks)

15 In the diagram, RT and PT are tangents to the circle.

Calculate:
a ∠ROP

b ∠RSP

c ∠RQP.

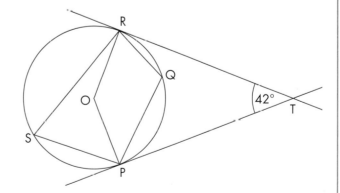

(6 marks)

CALCULATOR PAPER

These sample questions are similar to those you may meet in your GCSE examination. Try answering the questions. When you have finished, compare your answers with those given on pages 124-126 to see how well you have done.

Answer all the questions. You may use a calculator.

I   Aaron, Baljit and Carlie share £180 in the ratio 2 : 3 : 5.
How much is Carlie's share?

(2 marks)

2   **a** Simplify these.
    (i) $a^3 \times a^5$

    (ii) $\dfrac{b^8}{b^3}$

  b Multiply out $(3x^2y)(xy^3)$.

(4 marks)

3   Damian is investigating the numbers of CDs that his friends have bought.
He designs a data collection sheet.
This is one of his questions.

How many CDs have you bought?
(Tick one box)
☐   ☐   ☐   ☐   ☐
0–10   10–20   20–30   30–40   40 +

Write down **two** things that are wrong with this question.

(2 marks)

4 A school entered 144 pupils for languages.
The numbers are shown in the table.

Language	Number of pupils
French	36
German	80
Spanish	28

Draw a pie chart to show the languages entries. Label each sector clearly.

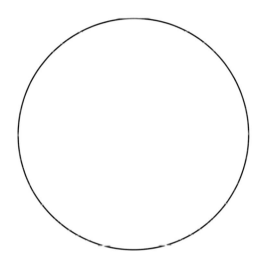

(3 marks)

5 The travel graph shows the journey
of a train between two towns A and C,
stopping at B.

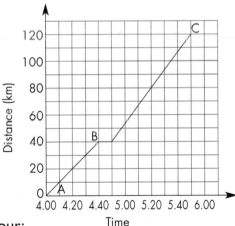

Use the graph to find, in kilometres per hour:
a the average speed between towns A and B

b the average speed between towns A and C.

(3 marks)

6 In triangle ABC, the length of side AB is 7.5 cm.
   Angle A is 60° and angle C is 80°.
   Make an accurate drawing of triangle ABC.

(2 marks)

7 Use your calculator to work out the value of each expression.
   Write down all the figures on your calculator, each time.
   Then give your answers correct to three significant figures (3 s.f.).

   a $\dfrac{4.85}{3.23 \times 5.62}$

   b $\sqrt{5 - \pi}$

(4 marks)

8 **a** Mrs Boad's bill for repairs to her car was £88 plus VAT.
      VAT is charged at 17.5%. What was her total bill?

   b Mr Ridgway's bill for car repairs was £176.25 including VAT.
      How much was the bill before the VAT was added?

(5 marks)

9 Complete this table and draw the graph of $y = x^3 + x$ for values of x from $^-2$ to 3.

x	$^-2$	$^-1$	0	1	2	3
y			0	2	10	30

On the graph paper below, draw the graph of $y = x^3 + x$ for the values in the table.

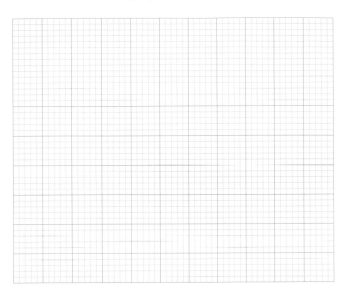

Use trial and improvement to find, correct to 1 decimal place, a solution for $x^3 + x = 12$ that lies between $x = 2$ and $x = 3$.

(3 marks)

10 Simplify the expression $(x + 3)^2 - (x - 3)^2$.

(3 marks)

11 A circular photo frame is shown opposite.
The diameter of the photo is **6 cm** and
the outer diameter of the frame is **12 cm**.
Calculate the area of the frame.

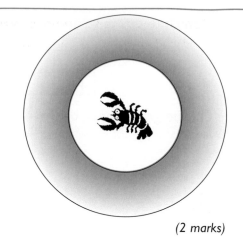

(2 marks)

12 ABC is a triangle.
Angle *B* is twice angle *A*.
Angle *C* is 8° more than angle *A*.
a Form an equation to show this information.

b Solve your equation to find the value of *A*.

(4 marks)

13 In the diagram, which is not drawn accurately,
O is the centre of the circle.

a Calculate the value of *p*.
Give a reason for your answer.

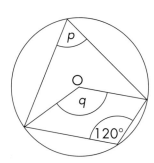

b Calculate the value of *q*.
Give a reason for your answer.

(4 marks)

14 A vertical cliff is 485 metres high. The angle of depression from the top of the cliff of a boat at sea is 20°. What is the distance of the boat from the foot of the cliff?

(3 marks)

15 Dr Habib wants to buy a car. She collects information about engine capacity and fuel consumption and draws up a table like this.

Engine capacity (litres)	Fuel consumption (mpg)
2.6	20.0
2.0	27.5
1.2	34.5
1.6	32.0
3.0	19.5
1.8	28.5
1.4	33.5

a Plot this information on a scatter graph and draw the line of best fit.

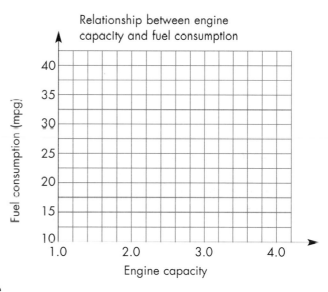

Relationship between engine capacity and fuel consumption

b Use your line of best fit to estimate the fuel consumption of a car with an engine capacity of:
  (i) 2.3 litres

  (ii) 3.5 litres.

c Explain why one of these two estimates is more reliable than the other.

(6 marks)

EXAM PRACTICE: ANSWERS

Non-calculator paper

1   **a** **(i)** $2^5 = 32$ **(ii)** $3^3 = 27$
   b 2 and $^-5$
   Comments
   a $2^5 = 2 \times 2 \times 2 \times 2 \times 2 = 32$
      $3^3 = 3 \times 3 \times 3 = 27$
   b The term-to-term rule is 'subtract 7'.
      $9 - 7 = 2$
      $2 - 7 = ^-5$

2   8×10^1 km² (square kilometres)
   Comments
   Area per head of population
   $= \dfrac{4 \times 10^{11}}{5 \times 10^9} = 0.8 \times 10^2 = 8 \times 10^1$ km²,
   leaving the answer in standard form.

3   **a** p(green) = 0.1
   b 20
   Comments
   a p(green) = 1 − (0.4 + 0.5)
      Use the fact that total probability = 1.
   b Number of blue discs = 50 × 0.4 = 20

4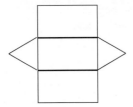
   Comments
   The net should be drawn, using the fact that the cross-section is an equilateral triangle. The lengths should be drawn to the required accuracy of ±1mm and angles should be drawn to the required accuracy of ±1°.

5   The data can be represented as a single stem-and-leaf diagram like this.

Article A		Article B
	2	8 9
9 9 8 6 2	3	0 1 3 4 6 6 7 8 8 9
9 7 7 5 5 4 4 3 3 1	4	0 1 1 2 2 6
1 0 0	5	

   Key for A: 9 | 3 = 39
      for B: 2 | 8 = 28
   Comments
   From the stem-and-leaf diagram you can see that the paragraphs in article A are generally longer than the paragraphs in article B.

6   $y = 3x - 4$
   Comments
   Substitute values for the points (3, 5) and (1, $^-1$) in the equation $y = mx + c$.
   $5 = 3m + c$
   $-1 = 1m + c$
   Use the process of elimination.
   Subtract one equation from the other to produce $6 = 2m$ so $m = 3$.
   Substitute this value into the first equation to give $c = ^-4$.

7   **a** $x < 3$
   b $x < 5\frac{1}{3}$
   Comments
   a $4x - 3 < 9$
      $4x < 12$ — Adding 3 to both sides.
      $x < 4$ — Dividing both sides by 4.
   b $11 + 2x > 5x - 5$
      $11 > 3x - 5$ — Subtracting $2x$ from both sides.
      $16 > 3x$ — Adding 5 to both sides.
      $\frac{16}{3} > x$ — Dividing both sides by 3.
      $x < 5\frac{1}{3}$ — Making x the subject of the inequality.

8   **a** 1   **b** No
   Comments
   a Show that $36 \times \frac{1}{36} = 1$.
   b The answer 'No' must be accompanied by an example. $^-1 \leqslant$ answer $\leqslant$ $^+1$

9   **a** $36 = 2^2 \times 3^2$
   b HCF = 12
   Comments
   You can find the HCF by repeatedly dividing by prime numbers.
   Here $36 = 2 \times 2 \times 3 \times 3 = 2^2 \times 3^2$
   Similarly $60 = 2 \times 2 \times 3 \times 5 = 2^2 \times 3 \times 5$
   So the HCF $= 2^2 \times 3 = 12$

10   $2\pi r(r + h)$
   Comments
   $2\pi r$ is a common factor and is taken outside the brackets.

11   Volume = 360π cm³
   Comments
   For the cylinder,
   volume = $\pi r^2 h$
      $= \pi \times 6^2 \times 10$ Where $r = \frac{1}{2} \times$ diameter.
      $= 360\pi$ cm³ Leaving the answer in terms of π.

12 $x = 7$ cm or $2\frac{2}{7}$ cm

Comments

$\dfrac{14}{x} = \dfrac{8}{4}$

$\dfrac{x}{14} = \dfrac{4}{8}$ Turning the expressions upside-down.

$x = \dfrac{4}{8} \times 14$

$x = 7$

$\dfrac{14}{4} = \dfrac{8}{x}$

$\dfrac{4}{14} = \dfrac{x}{8}$ Turning the expressions upside-down.

$x = \dfrac{4}{14} \times 8 = \dfrac{32}{14} = \dfrac{16}{7} = 2\frac{2}{7}$

The way that the question is asked does suggest the possibility of more than one solution as it says 'possible values'. Always take care to check whether a second solution exists.

13 The expression $\frac{1}{3}\pi$ is a constant and r^4 does not give units of volume so the formula cannot represent the volume.

Comments

Ignoring constants, you should be able to identify lengths, areas and volumes.

14 a 19   **b** 16

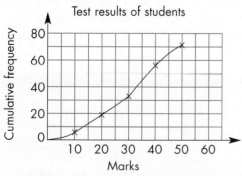

Test results of students

c Median = 33 and interquartile range = 21
d The interquartile range is bigger so the results are more spread out in the second test.

Comments

a Read 19 from the table.
b Calculate 16 as $72 - 56$.

Marks	Cumulative frequency	Frequency
< 10	6	6
< 20	19	13
< 30	33	14
< 40	56	23
< 50	72	16

When plotting the cumulative frequency diagram, remember to plot the points at the upper class boundaries (i.e. 10, 20, 30, 40 and 50).

c Median = 33
Lower quartile = 19
Upper quartile = 40
Interquartile range = $40 - 19 = 21$
Always show your working, so that the examiner can see where your answers come from.

d The conclusions should be stated clearly.

15 a $\angle ROP = 138°$
  b $\angle RSP = 69°$
  c $\angle RQP = 111°$

Comments

a $\angle OPT = \angle ORT = 90°$
As the tangents to a circle are perpendicular to the radius at the point of contact.
$\angle ROP - 360°$ $(42° + 90° + 90°)$
As the angles of quadrilateral RTPO add up to 360°.
$\angle ROP = 138°$

b $\angle RSP = \frac{1}{2} \times \angle ROP$
The angle subtended at the circumference of a circle equals half of the angle subtended at the centre by the same arc.

c $\angle RQP = 180° - \angle RSP$
Opposite angles of cyclic quadrilateral RQPS add up to 180°.
$\angle RQP = 180° - 69° = 111°$
Remember that the diagrams in these questions will not be drawn accurately so you should not attempt to reach solutions by using measuring instruments.

Calculator paper

1 £90

Comments

The total number of shares is $2 + 3 + 5 = 10$

Each share is £180 ÷ 10 = £18

Carlie has five shares at £18 = £90.

2 **a** **(i)** a^8 **(ii)** b^5

 b $3x^3y^4$

Comments

 a **(i)** $a^3 \times a^5 = a^{3+5} = a^8$

 Using the laws of indices.

 (ii) $\dfrac{b^8}{b^3} = b^{8-3} = b^5$

 Using the laws of indices.

 b $(3x^2y)(xy^3) = 3 \times x^2 \times y \times x \times y^3$

 $= 3 \times x^2 \times x \times y \times y^3$

 $= 3 \times x^3 \times y^4$

 $= 3x^3y^4$

3 There is no time scale.

The ranges of numbers overlap.

Comments

Remember to be descriptive about things that are wrong.

Think about questions that might be misunderstood.

Damian does not give a time interval.

What was the time scale over which the CDs were bought – a week, a month, a year?

The ranges of the numbers in the groups all overlap so where do you record a total of 10 CDs – in the 0–10 group or the 10–20 group?

4

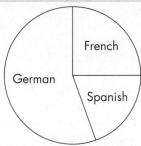

Comments

Language	Number of pupils	Angle
French	36	$\frac{36}{144} \times 360° = 90°$
German	80	$\frac{80}{144} \times 360° = 200°$
Spanish	28	$\frac{28}{144} \times 360° = 70°$

Check that the angles add up to 360°.

Remember to label each sector and include the angles at the centre for further information.

5 **a** 60 kph

 b 65.5 kph (3 s.f.)

Comments

 a For speed in kilometres per hour, the time must be expressed in hours.

 40 minutes = $\frac{40}{60}$ hours

 Between A and B distance travelled = 40 km and time taken = 40 minutes.

 So speed = distance ÷ time

 $= 40 \div \frac{40}{60}$

 $= 60$ kph

 b Again 110 minutes = $\frac{110}{60}$ hours.

 Between A and C distance travelled = 120 km and time taken = 110 minutes.

 So speed = distance ÷ time = $120 \div \frac{110}{60}$

 $= 65.454\,545 = 65.5$ kph (3 s.f.)

6 Draw triangle ABC with side AB = 7.5 cm.

$A = 60°$ and $C = 88°$

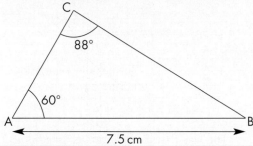

Comments

The triangle should be constructed with a ruler and a protractor.

The lengths should be drawn to the required accuracy of ±1 mm and angles drawn to the required accuracy of ±1°.

7 **a** 0.267 179 357 227… = 0.267 (3 s.f.)

 b 1.363 234 15… = 1.36 (3 s.f.)

Comments

You need to familiarise yourself with your calculator.

Check the √ and the π buttons.

Always use approximations to check your answer.

8   **a** £103.40   **b** £150

> *Comments*
>
> **a** An increase of 17.5% represents 117.5%
> (100% + 17.5%) of the original bill so:
> 1% of £88 = £0.88
> 117.5% = 117.5 × £0.88 = £103.40
>
> **b** After an increase of 17.5%, £176.25
> represents 117.5% (100% + 17.5%) of the
> original bill so:
> 117.5% of bill = £176.25
> 1% of bill = £1.50   Dividing by 117.5.
> 100% of bill = £150   Multiplying by 100.

9   Completing this table:

x	$^-2$	$^-1$	0	1	2	3
y	$^-10$	$^-2$	0	2	10	30

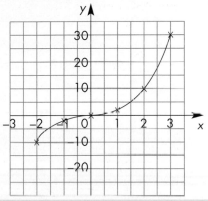

> *Comments*
> Remember that $(^-2)^3 + {}^-2 = {}^-8 + {}^-2 = {}^-10$
> and $(^-1)^3 + {}^-1 = {}^-1 + {}^-1 = {}^-2$
> Use trial and improvement to home in on the
> solution.
> Try $x = 2.5$
> $x^3 + x = 18.125$ too high
> Try $x = 2.1$
> $x^3 + x = 11.361$ too low
> Try $x = 2.2$
> $x^3 + x = 12.848$ too high
> Try $x = 2.15$
> $x^3 + x = 12.088\,375$ too high
> Therefore x must be between 2.1 and 2.15
> which will always be 2.1 to 1 d.p.
> Remember to show all of your working.

10 $12x$

> *Comments*
> $(x + 3)^2 - (x - 3)^2 = \{x^2 + 6x + 9\} - \{x^2 - 6x + 9\}$
> $= x^2 + 6x + 9 - x^2 + 6x - 9$
> $= 12x$

11   Area of the frame = 84.8 cm² (3 s.f.)

> *Comments*
> Calculate the area of the frame by subtracting
> the area of the smaller circle from the area of
> the larger circle, remembering to halve the
> diameter to give the radius each time.
> Area = $\pi \times 6^2 - \pi \times 3^2 = 84.823\,002$ cm²

12   **a** $x + 2x + x + 8 = 180$ or equivalent
       b $x = 43$

> *Comments*
> Let angle A be $x°$.
> Angle B is twice angle A so angle B is $2x°$.
> Angle C is 8° more than angle A so angle C is
> $(x + 8)°$.
> The angles of a triangle add up to 180° so:
> $A + B + C = 180°$
> $x + 2x + x + 8 = 180$
> Solving the equation:
> $x + 2x + x + 8 = 180$
> $4x + 8 = 180$ Simplifying.
> $4x = 172$ Subtracting 8 from both
>   sides.
> $x = 43$ Dividing both sides by 4.

13   **a** $p = 60°$ **b** $q = 120°$

> *Comments*
> **a** $p = 60°$
> Opposite angles of a cyclic quadrilateral add
> up to 180°.
> **b** $q = 120°$
> The angle subtended at the centre is twice
> that subtended at the circumference, by the
> same arc.
> You need to be fully aware of the properties of
> circles.

14   Distance = 1330 m (3 s.f.)

> *Comment*
> Start by drawing a sketch of the situation and
> completing the given details on the diagram.
> Since the angle of depression is 20° the top
> angle in the triangle is 70° (as angles forming a
> right angle add up to 90°). Then from the
> triangle:
> $\tan 70° = \dfrac{x}{485}$
> $x = 485 \times \tan 70° = 1332.5265$ m

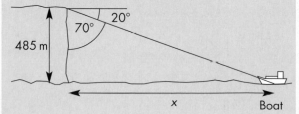

15 a

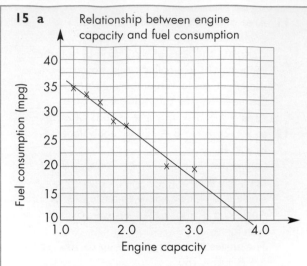

Relationship between engine capacity and fuel consumption

b (i) 24 mpg   **(ii)** 13 mpg

c The first value is better as it lies within the plotted points, whereas the second value lies at the ends of the plotted points and is therefore more likely to be incorrect.

Comments
You should use a line of best fit to find estimates for the given questions.
You will be awarded better marks if you provide a full explanation for your choice.
Always take account of the marks allocated to the question.
This should give you an idea of how much detail to provide.